THE NEW! GET RID OF BOAT ODORS!

A Boat Owner's Guide to Marine Sanitation Systems and Other Sources of Aggravation and Odor
Second Edition

PEGGIE HALL
"THE HEADMISTRESS"

SEAWORTHY PUBLICATIONS, INC.
Cocoa Beach, FL

The NEW Get Rid of Boat Odors

A Boat Owners Guide to Marine Sanitation Systems and
Other Sources of Aggravation and Odor

Second Edition

Copyright © 2016 by Peggie Hall

Printed and bound in the United States of America. All rights reserved. Except
for use in review, no part of this book may be reproduced in any form or by any
electronic or mechanical means including information storage and retrieval systems
without written permission from the publisher.
For rights inquires, or to contact the publisher:

Seaworthy Publication, Inc.
2023 N. Atlantic Ave., Unit #226
Cocoa Beach, FL 32931
Phone: 312-610-3634
Email: orders@seaworthy.com

Visit us on the Web at: http://www.seaworthy.com

Library of Congress Cataloging-in-Publication Data

Names: Hall, Peggie, 1942- author.
Title: The new get rid of boat odors! : a boat owner's guide to marine
  sanitation systems and other sources of aggravation and odor / Peggie
  Hall, "The Headmistress".
Other titles: Get rid of boat odors. | boat owner's guide to marine
  sanitation systems and other sources of aggravation and odor
Description: 2nd edition. | Cocoa Beach, FL : Seaworthy Publications, Inc.,
  [2016] | Includes index.
Identifiers: LCCN 2015050114 (print) | LCCN 2015051472 (ebook) | ISBN
  9781892399786 (pbk. : alk. paper) | ISBN 1892399784 (pbk. : alk. paper) |
  |

  ISBN 9781892399793 (e-book) | ISBN 1892399792 (e-book)
Subjects: LCSH: Boats and boating--Waste disposal. | Boats and
  boating--Equipment and supplies. | Odor control.
Classification: LCC VM481 .H35 2016 (print) | LCC VM481 (ebook) | DDC
  623.8/546--dc23
LC record available at http://lccn.loc.gov/2015050114

Design by Brian Murphy, Digital Dreamland
Book design and composition by Shauna McPherson

Peggie Hall is nationally recognized in the boating industry as one of the few experts in marine sanitation, and is often referred to as "the Head Mistress." She has written a number of articles for major boating magazines, is often asked to speak at conferences and conduct seminars for various organizations and at major boat shows, and has been a consultant to a number of state agencies. For more than 20 years she also hosted plumbing and sanitation forums on many online boating sites, beginning even before the internet as we know it today existed with the Sailing Forum on CompuServe. Her comprehensive article "Marine Sanitation: Fact vs. Folklore," first published in 1994, was long considered the most definitive guide to US marine sanitation laws, various types of sanitation equipment, proper installation, operation, maintenance and odor control ever written. Her book "Get Rid of Boat Odors! – A Boat Owner's Guide to Marine Sanitation Systems and Other Sources of Aggravation and Odor," was the first, and still the only, book ever written devoted entirely to that subject and has been a best seller, not only in the U.S., but in every English speaking country.

She first entered the marine business in 1987, when she formed Peal Products, which was the first company in the marine industry to focus exclusively on onboard sewage management issues and the elimination of odors on boats. In addition to the Peal Products line of environmentally friendly sanitation and cleaning products (which were soon given outstanding performance ratings by *Powerboat Reports* and *Practical Sailor*), Peal Products was a distributor for every major U.S. manufacturer of marine toilets, MSDs, and related equipment and accessories. As a member of ABYC, she was a member of a sanitation project technical committee formed to establish a standard for sanitation equipment and installation onboard from its inception in 1991 through 1996. In 1999 Mrs. Hall sold the Peal Products product line to Raritan Engineering, a major manufacturer of sanitation equipment. She is now an independent consultant.

Disclaimer: *Peggie Hall is not in any way associated with any product or equipment manufacturer, nor does she receive any compensation what so ever for recommending any product or manufacturer. Her opinions are her own and her recommendations are based on her own experience and that of boat owners over several decades.*

ACKNOWLEDGMENTS

Everyone in the marine sanitation industry and countless boat owners too have contributed something of value to my storehouse of knowledge that's the basis for this new updated and expanded "Get Rid of Boat Odors," and I'm grateful to every one of you! But the most helpful person over my entire 25 year career was Vic Willman, who retired from Raritan after more than 40 years of service that included a stint as their plant manager followed by a couple of decades as their tech services manager, and was the most patient teacher anyone could ask for.

Thanks too to Bosworth Marine Products, Dometic, Forespar Products, Groco, Raritan Engineering, and Thetford Marine for the photos and illustrations throughout this book and for permission to use their trademarks.

CONTENTS

INTRODUCTION

Ask any boat owner, "What's the most annoying problem on your boat," and the answer is invariably, "*odors!*" Ask which system causes the most problems, and the answer is invariably, "the *head!*" Ask what causes the odors, and most people answer again, "the head!" They'd only be half-right. Sometimes it *is* the head that's the source of boat odors, but odors aren't the only source of aggravation on a boat. Nothing can ruin a cruise, or even a day on the water, faster than a toilet that stops up, or just stops working. It happens all too often, but it doesn't have to; 99% of problems can be prevented if you know how and prevention is always easier than cure. It's not rocket science—in fact, it's really very simple once you understand the basic principles. But few people do. Almost no one wants to specialize in boat plumbing, especially sanitation plumbing—in fact, it's a part of the marine industry most people try to avoid. Consequently, very few people know anything about it—which is why so much misinformation is circulated. Where does all the misinformation come from? Most of it can best be categorized as folklore: it's been said so often by so many people, it's just accepted as "fact."

And that's why I wrote this book. Not only to help boat owners find and eliminate all the real sources of boat odors, but also to de-mystify what is for many the single most confounding, aggravating and annoying system on their boats: the marine sanitation system!

part I

WHAT'S LEGAL, WHAT'S NOT

U.S. MARINE SANITATION LAWS

(The following is a summary of the U.S. federal marine sanitation laws pertaining to privately owned recreational vessels that are in effect at the time this book was published. If you're determined to read them in all their glorious "legalese," go to the Code of Federal Regulations 40 CFR 140.1-3, and 33 CFR 159.7

TWO IMPORTANT DEFINITIONS

U.S. marine sanitation laws pertain only to vessels, which are defined by the Code of Federal Regulations as "every description of watercraft or other artificial conveyance used, or capable of being used, as a means of transportation upon the navigable waters of the United States." In other words, if it floats and was designed to move under its own power—whether or not it presently can—it's a "vessel." But permanently moored floating structures that were never intended to move are not vessels, and therefore are not subject to marine sanitation laws, but are subject to state and local laws.

Sewage is the other operative word in U.S. marine sanitation laws. The CFR defines sewage from a vessel as "human body wastes and the waste from toilets and other receptacles intended to receive or retain body wastes." No matter how sewage may be defined in any other context, that's the complete definition of sewage as it pertains to vessels. It doesn't include garbage, trash, gray water ("galley, bath or shower water"), or bilge water. Sewage is human body waste, period.

Now...let's get on with the laws pertaining to sewage from vessels:
It is illegal to discharge untreated sewage into *any* U.S. waters. Federal law defines "discharge" as "includes, but is not limited to, any spilling, leaking, pouring, pumping, emitting, emptying, or dumping." That means it is illegal to discharge toilet waste directly overboard from the toilet. It's also illegal to dump a holding tank, bucket or anything else into any U.S. waters. Untreated is raw sewage directly from the toilet or holding tank. Only waste that goes directly overboard from a USCG certified Type I or Type II MSD is considered treated waste.

To legally flush a toilet directly overboard or dump a holding tank, you must be at least 3 miles (6 to 12 miles in parts of the Gulf of Mexico) offshore—and that doesn't mean 3 miles from the nearest shore in a river, lake, bay or sound. It means 3 miles out to sea, away from the nearest point of land on the whole North American coastline or any of its offshore islands.

In waters that are designated "no discharge" all vessels with toilet facilities must be equipped with a holding tank, and all toilet waste must flush only into it to be held for pump-out or discharge later at sea beyond the "3 mile limit." However, "no discharge" only applies to toilet waste. "Gray water" (galley, bath and shower water) may legally be discharged overboard except where specifically prohibited; (Currently gray water discharge is prohibited in only a few inland lakes and in small specifically designated waters within the Florida Keys National Marine Sanctuary where there are particularly fragile reefs.)

Where the discharge of treated sewage is allowed, the vessel must be equipped with, and use, a Coast Guard Certified Type I or II Marine Sanitation Device (MSD) which treats the waste to standards prescribed by law in the Code of Federal Regulations.

Important Note: No marine toilet (head), by itself, is a Coast Guard Certified Type I or II MSD All Coast Guard Certified Type I and II MSDs are separate treatment devices. The head (toilet) itself only receives and discharges sewage, it doesn't retain or treat it; the devices which retain and/ or treat sewage are always separate from the toilet. It is these devices which must be certified by the Coast Guard that they treat sewage to the standards prescribed by law for overboard discharge.

TYPE I STANDARDS

The discharge from a Type I MSD must be macerated to the extent that there are no visible solids; in other words, pureed into liquid. The maximum allowable bacteria count is 1,000 per 100 milliliter.

TYPE II STANDARDS

The discharge from a Type II MSD may not have a bacteria count greater than 200 per 100 milliliter, and suspended solids may not exceed 150 mg./100 milliliter (Think 100 grains of instant coffee in a cupful of water).

TYPE III STANDARDS

A Type III MSD is a holding tank. Any container that can receive and retain sewage (toilet waste) is considered automatically certified. Vessels under 66' may use a Type I, II or III; vessels 66' and larger may only use a Type II or III.

How do you know whether your boat is equipped with a Coast Guard approved MSD? Obviously, you'll know whether you have a Type III if you know whether or not the boat has a holding tank. All Type I's and Type II's must have a Coast Guard Certification label, affixed by the manufacturer. The label must show the name of the manufacturer, the name and model number of the device, the month and year of manufacture, the type of MSD, a certification number and a certification statement. If there is no label, the device is not a CG Certified MSD (treatment device).

Only waste that is treated by a Coast Guard Certified Type I or Type II MSD is considered "treated" waste; there is nothing that can be added to a holding tank that will make it legal to dump the tank. In fact, even if the waste has been through a treatment device before going into a holding tank, the tank still cannot legally be dumped inside the "3 mile limit." Nor can a boat owner design and use his own treatment device; even if it does meet all the legal requirements, only devices submitted to the Coast Guard by equipment manufacturers who then must manufacture every unit exactly to the certified specifications are legal.

There is a common misconception that all this can be gotten around by using a bucket instead of the toilet and tossing the contents of the bucket overboard. Unfortunately, this is just a myth. As stated in the definitions above, "discharge includes, but is not limited to, any spilling, leaking, pouring, pumping, emitting, emptying, or dumping," which makes the "bucket and chuck it," method of waste management just as illegal as dumping a holding tank.

However, should you choose to stand at the rail and urinate or defecate directly into the water, or jump into the water to do it, you may run afoul of some laws regarding indecent exposure, but you will not be in violation of any marine sanitation law. It's only when the waste is put into a container first, or flushed through an installed device aboard that any law is violated.

*The only marine toilets that were also Type 1 MSDs were recirculating toilets-the Monogram Monomatic and the Danforth. Although a few still survive, both have been out of production for nearly 30 years and are so obsolete that no parts or even the chemicals are still available, so they are no longer usable as legal treatment devices.

ACCEPTABLE MEANS OF SECURING THE SYSTEMS

In coastal waters that provide immediate access to open sea, a boat may be equipped with diverter valves—commonly called "Y-valves"—that allow the tank to be dumped or the toilet to be flushed directly overboard at sea. The law only requires that the system be "secured from accidental illegal discharge" while inside the "3 Mile Limit;" and there are a number of ways a system can be secured; which are legal for your boat depends upon whether your boat is equipped with a Type I or II MSD (treatment device) or a Type III (holding tank).

If your toilet is connected to a Type I or II MSD, U.S. federal law (33 CFR 159.7) lists the following acceptable methods of securing the device:
(1) Closing the seacock and removing the handle;
(2) Padlocking the seacock in the closed position;
(3) Using a non-releasable wire-tie to hold the seacock in the closed position; or
(4) Locking the door to the space enclosing the toilets with a padlock or door handle key lock.

If your toilet is connected to a holding tank, acceptable methods of securing the device include:
(1) Closing each valve leading to an overboard discharge and removing the handle;
(2) Padlocking each valve leading to an overboard discharge in the closed position; or
(3) Using a non-releasable wire-tie to hold each valve leading to an overboard discharge in the closed position.

Inland may be another story. The Great Lakes and all non-navigable inland lakes are "no discharge" waters. They're also a loooong way from the ocean. Since there's no possible way to legally use a y-valve or macerator to dump a tank, many states have made it illegal for vessels operating on these waters even to have one or both installed. When in doubt, check with your local authorities.

TYPE I MSD:

The Raritan ElectroScan is the current version of the Raritan LectraSan, which has been the most popular Type I MSD since it was introduced in 1974; it can be used with any toilet. It uses no chemicals; instead electrodes charge the ions in salt water, creating a type of chlorine that kills bacteria. Designed for use in salt water, it also can be used in brackish and fresh water, and with toilets designed to use fresh water by adding the appropriate optional salt feed tank to the system or by manually adding salt to each flush.

Groco ThermaPure2
Photo courtesy of Groco

In 1992, Raritan introduced the PuraSan. Although originally designed for use in fresh water, it can also be used, and works just as well, in brackish or salt water. The PuraSan does not have an electrode pack, so it does not produce its own chlorine. Instead flush water passes through a cartridge containing a solid halogen tablet (2

Raritan Type 1
Photo courtesy of Raritan Engineering

tablets in the newest version of the cartridge), carrying enough chemical away with it to treat to legal overboard discharge standards. (Raritan insists on calling this cartridge a "tablet dispenser," which misleads many people into thinking that it delivers chlorine "pills" into the bowl or treatment device. It does not; water flows through the cartridge, washing away a little of the chemical with each flush.)

Both the ElectroScan or Electro Scan and the PuraSan treat one flush at a time; they are "flow through" devices that discharge by overflowing an amount of treated waste that's equal to the volume of new incoming waste The ElectroScan or Electro Scan runs for approximately three minutes after each flush, and consumes approximately 1.7 amp hours. Because the PuraSan has no electrodes, its power consumption is about half that of the ElectroScan or Electro Scan. Neither has any holding capacity, and neither is acceptable for use in "no discharge" waters. Since the chlorine is either created or an integral part of the system, it is not necessary to carry any chemicals for use in either device.

No bleach or any other chemical household cleaning or toilet bowl product should ever be used in a system in which a ElectroScan or Electro Scan or PuraSan is installed. Use only cleaning products recommended by Raritan.

The Groco ThermoPure-2 is a USCG Type-1 MSD that uses no chemicals but instead uses heat to kill bacteria accomplished by pumping macerated waste through a chamber where low-level heat is introduced to eliminate bacteria. No chemicals or additives are required and treatment is equally efficient in fresh, brackish or salt water. It can be used with any toilet system. However, because it needs both AC power and DC power, it's only practical on larger boats.

The SeaLand SanX (originally the Mansfield TDX and after 1984 the SeaLand TDX) was discontinued by the manufacturer in 2002, but is included here because it can still be found on some boats as of this writing. It consists of a 9 gallon tank equipped with an internal macerator, a holder for the gallon jug of TDX (the only chemical certified for use with it) and a chemical pump that automatically injects TDX when the treatment cycle is initiated. No parts or technical support are still available. However, the "T-Series Waste Discharge Pump" which was sold separately is still in production, as is the chemical TDX.

The SanX was designed to be plumbed for both pump-out and/or overboard discharge, making it both a Type I MSD (treatment device) and Type III MSD (holding tank). The toilet is plumbed to the SanX tank and sewage is held without treatment until a decision is made to either "treat and discharge" or have the tank pumped out. The "treat and discharge" mode is manually activated by a switch, so it uses no power except during this cycle, which lasts for 20 minutes. It begins by automatically injecting a formaldehyde-based chemical called TDX. The macerator mixes the chemical and liquefies the tank contents, after which the tank may either be pumped overboard automatically by the SeaLand "T-Pump" or by using a manual pump. When used as a Type III (pump-out only), it is not necessary to activate the treatment cycle.

The chemical SanX/TDX (by that brand name), a nasty formaldehyde-based "witches brew" that requires very careful storage and handling, is the only chemical approved for use in the TDX or SanX; therefore a supply must be carried aboard. It is available only in 1-gallon jugs; each treatment cycle uses one quart.

When choosing a Type I device, there are several important considerations: the amount of space required, whether that space is located within the manufacturer's specifications for distance and path of the hoses, the amount of electrical current available to power it, and availability of parts and service. Although Headhunter and other manufacturers also offer Type I MSDs, the Lectra/San, PuraSan and SanX are by far the most widely used, but any Type I MSD can easily be installed by the boat owner in most cases.

TYPE II MSD

The four most well-known manufacturers of Type II MSDs are Raritan Engineering, Galley Maid, Microfor, and Headhunter. Because Type II systems are considerably more complex than Type I systems, and almost always involve multiple toilet installation, we recommend you consult with a qualified factory expert for advice about installing.

Raritan Managerm
Photo courtesy of Raritan Engineering

TYPE III MSD

A Type III MSD is a holding tank—originally defined in the CFR (Code of Federal Regulations) as "any container that receives and holds sewage and flush water at ambient temperatures, but does not discharge waste," now defined in the CFR as "a device that is designed to prevent the overboard discharge of treated or untreated sewage or any waste derived from sewage." That includes portapotties, composters, incinerating toilets, bladders, even 55 gallon drums. Holding tanks are considered automatically certified under a clause in the Coast Guard regulations and therefore will not have a certification label attached. Regrettably, this definition makes it legal, though not advisable, to store sewage in any container, whether or not the container is suitable for that use.

The EPA maintains an up-to-date list of "no discharge" waters on the internet at http://www.epa.gov/owow/oceans/regulatory/vessel

THE *NEW* GET RID OF BOAT ODORS

part II

CHOOSING AND INSTALLING A SYSTEM

There is no single "best toilet," only the best toilet for an individual boat and its owner. And there are a number of factors that go into selecting the best toilet for any boat: Boat size, power resources, holding tank size vs. flush water consumption, availability of accessible pump-out facilities, whether treatment is an option or not, who'll be using it—only adult "seasoned salts" or children and frequent landlubber/guests, space available, your budget, and even how long you plan to keep the current boat. Since the only thing that affects a boat's resale value is whether the toilet is in good working condition, it makes no sense to spend top dollar for a toilet on a boat you plan to sell in a year or two.

Any electric toilet would be a poor choice for a small boat with limited power resources. Even a manual toilet and a remote holding tank along with all the related plumbing may eat up more storage space on most boats under 28 feet than anyone wants to give up, making a self-contained system the best option.

On the other hand, a portapotty or even a manual toilet probably wouldn't be the best choice for most 30' or larger powerboats because people who own larger boats want appliances that are a bit more "upscale" than a portapotty and provide more creature comfort and convenience than they'd get from pumping a manual toilet.

MANUAL TOILETS

Even when it comes to choosing a manual toilet, there's a wide range in price, quality and user-friendliness. For decades the Wilcox-Crittenden "Skipper" was the Rolls Royce of manual marine toilets made in the U.S.—a bronze "throne" that had a price tag of about $1,000, designed to last 100 years or more with even minimal maintenance. Right behind it in price and quality were the W-C Imperial and Junior, and the Groco models EB and K. Wilcox-Crittenden was bought by Thetford/Norcold in 2003, who then discontinued the entire W-C product line, leaving the Groco Model K as the last "bronze throne" standing. That is, unless you count the British-made "Baby Blake," which has a price tag of over $6,000 at today's rate of exchange with the British pound.

At the other end of the spectrum are the compact manual toilets, only three of which are still made in the U.S. at the time of this writing—Raritan Engineering's PHC and Fresh Head (introduced in 2014, the Raritan Fresh Head is the first manual toilet designed to use onboard pressurized fresh water), and the Groco HF. Jabsco toilets, an American brand now owned by Xylem Flow Control, which was spun off from ITT in 2011, are now assembled in Mexico using components made in China and other countries that may or may not include the U.S. The Wilcox-Crittenden Headmate, the Raritan Compact, Compact II and Cricket have all been discontinued. Only some parts including "service" or "rebuild" kits still remain available for any Wilcox-Crittenden toilet as of this writing. All Groco, Raritan and Jabsco toilets that are still in production are fully supported with parts and technical assistance by their manufacturers, but as is true of most products, support for obsolete/discontinued toilet models only lasts for about 10 additional years.

In between the Groco Model K "bronze throne" and the compact manual toilets are just two full size manual toilets—the Raritan PH II and the Blakes Lavac, which is actually made in the UK by the same company that makes the "Baby Blake", but has a strong enough U.S. presence to be included here.

ELECTRIC TOILETS

There's also a huge range in the price, quality, durability and style of electric toilets, but price isn't necessarily an indicator of quality. There are two types of electric toilets: macerating and non-macerating and those that are designed to flush using "raw" water (sea, lake or river water), and those that are designed to use pressurized fresh water from the onboard fresh water supply.

The most basic electric toilets are the "hybrids"-manual toilets to which a motor has been added to replace the pump handle...and that's all it does. I don't recommend them because the pump is still a manual pump that-unlike macerating electric toilets-still requires all the maintenance needed by a manual toilet, in fact even more...because the motor pumps the toilet much faster, and with a much shorter stroke than pumping manually, which causes it to take longer to prime and therefore wears out the rubber o-rings etc. much faster...and also causes the toilet to "choke" on flushes that deliberate pumping manually can push through. They typically have a high amperage draw than most electric toilets and the combined prices of the toilet and motor is usually higher than a basic macerating electric toilet. They primarily appeal to sailors who want to have it both ways-the "push button convenience" of an electric toilet that can be converted to manual in the highly unlikely event of a catastrophic power failure. But if there isn't even the 10-15 amps needed to flush an electric toilet, there isn't likely to be enough to power navigation equipment, lights, communication equipment or anything else that needs power! But you will still have a bucket and line to dangle it over the side! So whether you can flush a toilet or have to resort to using the bucket should be the LEAST of your worries!

Macerating electric toilets, available in both raw and fresh water versions, have a blade similar to a blender blade that "purees" the solid waste and toilet paper as they go through it. The Dometic (formerly SeaLand) VacuFlush system uses accumulated vacuum created by an electric diaphragm pump to "suck" the waste out of the bowl. Some high-end mega-yacht toilets use water under high pressure.

Raw water macerating electric toilets have been around since the late 1960s. The early ones—some of which are still in production-were real power and water hogs that draw 30-50 amps and need 1-3 gallons of flush water. Today's typical raw water electric toilet only draws about 15 amps and uses an average of about a half-gallon (2 liters) of flush water. However, that can vary depending on how long you leave your finger on the flush button because the intake pump on the most basic models is usually an impeller type pump that's integral to the discharge pump. It must continue to draw in water the entire time the toilet is flushing because, if the water to the intake pump is cut off, dry friction heat "fries" the impeller. They also consume at least 50% more power, because it's the intake pump, not the discharge pump or macerator, that's the "power hog." It also makes most of the noise!

In 1978, Mansfield Plumbing developed the first toilet designed to flush with pressurized water from onboard fresh water supply. They named it the VacuFlush, and it was a real game changer because it was the only electric toilet that drew less than 6 amps per flush, needed less than 1-3 gallons of flush water and used onboard pressurized flush water, eliminating odors from sea water left to sit and stagnate in raw water toilets. In 1984, Mansfield spun off their marine division to a start-up called SeaLand Technology (now owned by a European company named Dometic). The SeaLand VacuFlush remained the only toilet designed to use fresh water until 1991 when the first macerating electric toilets designed to use pressurized flush water were introduced. Today, every toilet manufacturer offers a full selection of both raw and fresh water electric macerating toilets, all of which have a much lower current draw, need only about 2 quarts (I liter) of flush water, and are much quieter!

In salt water, flush water trapped and left to stagnate in the toilet intake line and pump can create odor problems—worse in some waters than in others especially in hot weather. The best solution may be a toilet designed to use onboard fresh water. On the other hand, if conserving fresh water is an issue, a toilet that uses onboard pressurized water may not be a good choice. However, on most fresh water rivers and lakes, intake odors aren't likely to be an issue, so choosing between a raw water toilet and a toilet designed to use pressurized flush water may only come down to current draw, noise...and price.

So when it comes to choosing the "best" toilet, there just isn't a "one size fits all" answer. But whether manual or electric, some toilets are just easier to operate and maintain than others—an important factor if you have small children and/or entertain landlubber guests frequently. Below are the various kinds of toilets, their advantages and drawbacks:

PORTAPOTTY

How it works:

Portapotties require no plumbing; they may or may not have a reservoir for flush water and chemical. Operation is simple: pull a lever that opens the "trap door" in the bowl to allow contents drain by gravity into a removable tank. Portapotties are available in 2-3 gallon and 5-6 gallon sizes. Those that include "MSD" as part of their model name/number can be permanently installed and fitted for pump-out—which I highly recommend for 5-6 gallon models because a full 5 gallon tank weighs almost 50 lbs.-a lot to try to carry off the boat when it needs emptying! And there's a lot more to recommend a 5-6 gallon "MSD" portapotty on boats up to about 28 feet. You'd need at least a 30 gal tank to hold the same number of flushes from a manual marine toilet. No plumbing is needed except a vent line and pump-out hose-so no new holes in the boat, and no tank and all the related plumbing using up to half your storage space. It needs zero maintenance except for rinsing out the tank-which you can do with a bucket while it's being pumped out. And all for about what you'd have to spend just for a new tank or a new toilet.

A highly upgraded self-contained "MSD" system is the SeaLand 711-M28 "Marine Traveler," which consists of a real toilet bowl atop its own 9-gallon tank which is fitted for pump-out, and uses pressurized water from the onboard system, but very little of it. Its only downside is the space needed for the tank footprint—approximately 20" x 20", which is too big to fit in the head on many smaller boats. But the "real" china bowl makes it good choice for larger boats too.

Portapotties and other self-contained systems are automatically CG Certified Type III MSDs.

Advantages:
   • Least expensive
   • Self-contained
   • Easy to operate-child/landlubber friendly
   • Available in two sizes: 2-3 gallon, 5-6 gallon
   • 2-3 gal. models hold 25-30 flushes, 5-6 gal. models hold 50-60 flushes
   • Uses minimal flush water stored in its own reservoir
   • Portable models require no plumbing
   • "MSD" versions need only a vent line and a pump-out line..

- Needs no power
- Needs no flush water thru-hull
- Fits in small spaces
- Portable models can be emptied anywhere there's a
  toilet to dump it into, no need to hunt for pump-out facilities
- "MSD" versions can also be permanently installed for pump-out,
  eliminating the need to carry it off the boat

Disadvantages:
- Carrying portable models off the boat can be a pain

Recommended for use on: boats up to 28' with very limited space for a remote holding tank and related plumbing

MANUAL MARINE TOILET

How they work:
(See more details in Part III "Flush With Success.")

Manual marine toilets are just what the name implies: the user must manually pump the toilet to pull flush water in and push bowl contents out. Most are simple dual action piston/cylinder pumps that pull in flush water and push it along with bowl contents out in a single up-down pump stroke. All but one—the Raritan "Fresh Head," introduced in 2014- are designed to use "raw" (sea, lake or river) water for flushing. Therefore, a below-waterline intake through-hull fitting and seacock is needed. They use no electricity. The user can control the amount of flush water used. Periodic lubrication and preventive maintenance (discussed later) is necessary.

Advantages:
- Less expensive than electric toilets
- Zero power consumption
- Available in sizes to fit very small spaces
- Wide range of quality and price
- Most use "raw" (sea or lake) water

Disadvantages:
- Can be daunting to landlubber guests and children
  who are unfamiliar with marine toilets
- Requires regular lubrication and maintenance
- Wide range of quality for price

Recommend for use on: sailboats with limited power resources and powerboats under 30'

ADDING A MOTOR TO A MANUAL TOILET

Owners of the Raritan PHII and the Groco Model K can "convert" their manual toilets to electric by adding a motor to them. Both the PHII and the Model K are outstanding MANUAL toilets, but adding a motor to them-or any other manual toilet-turns it into a horrible excuse for an electric toilet. Why? Because the motor only replaces the pump handle. The pump is still a manual pump that-unlike macerating electric toilets-still requires all the maintenance needed by a manual toilet. In fact it needs even more because the motor pumps the toilet much faster, and with a much shorter stroke than pumping manually, which causes it to take longer to prime. So unless you're scrupulous about always keeping the toilet properly lubricate, that wears out the rubber o-rings etc. much faster...and also causes the toilet to "choke" on flushes that deliberate pumping manually can push through. It also has a higher amperage draw than most electric toilets. I know a lot of

people who've added a motor and then wished they hadn't, who've opted to disconnect it again permanently and put the pump handle back on. Unfortunately, the PHE II also costs more than basic macerating electric toilets.

But for some reason sailors want to have it both ways–the "push button convenience" of an electric toilet that can be converted to manual in the event of a catastrophic power failure. But there's no REAL advantage to that, because if you don't even have enough power to flush an electric toilet, you don't have enough to run navigation equipment, lights, communication equipment or anything else that needs power either, but you DO still have a bucket and a line to drop it overboard! So whether you can flush a toilet or have to resort to using it is the LEAST of your worries! So if you want a manual toilet, both the Raritan PH II and the Groco Model K are excellent choices...but if you want an electric toilet, go with one that's designed to be an electric toilet from the ground up, not a "hybrid."

ELECTRIC TOILETS

How they work: *(See more details in the chapters in Part III "Flush With Success.")*

All older electric macerating toilets were designed to flush using raw water. Today, every manufacturer also offers models designed to use pressurized water from the onboard supply, and most also offer raw water models designed to use a fraction of the flush water their 'ancestors" needed.

In a raw water electric toilet, an intake pump–typically an impeller, but it can also be an electric diaphragm pump–pulls flush water in while a discharge pump—also typically an impeller–pushes bowl contents and flush water out. Between the two is a macerator blade that purees solid waste & paper—which, by the way, are the only things that should ever go into one!

Electric toilets designed to use onboard fresh water for flushing use less flush water and consume less power than any other type of toilet, and are also quieter than other electric toilets. Instead of an intake pump, the toilet is equipped with a solenoid and essential valves and protective devices that allow it to use pressurized water. That's the only difference in the way fresh water and raw water toilets work.

NOTE: only toilets that are designed to use pressurized water should ever be connected to the onboard fresh water system. Connecting a toilet that is not designed to use pressurized water can pollute the fresh water supply, damage the toilet or both, and every toilet manufacturer specifically warns against it in their installation instructions.

Manual to electric conversion kits:

Most toilet manufacturers offer "conversion kits" that replace the entire pump assembly with an electric macerating pump. The "kit" consists of everything but the bowl, seat and lid, allowing the owner to save money by "recycling" the bowl from the existing manual toilet or failed electric toilet. All bowls that mount using a 4-bolt "+" pattern—which is 99% of bowls— will fit almost every electric toilet "conversion kit."

Advantages:
- Less expensive than complete electric toilet
- "Push button" convenience
- Child/landlubber-friendly
- Macerated waste less likely to clog plumbing
- Most are available In both fresh water and sea water versions

Disadvantages:
- Some differences in quality and durability
- Some models use excessive amounts of flush water
- Power consumption of some electric toilets may exceed small boat resources

Recommended for use on any boat on which "push button convenience" is preferred over manual and which has sufficient power resources to support the 10-15 amp power draw.

VACUUM TOILETS
Advantages:
- The same as macerating electric toilets designed to use pressurized flush water
- Easy to use—just step on the pedal or push the button, so very child/landlubber friendly

Disadvantages:
- Price is higher than most fresh water electric macerating toilets
- Components (vacuum tank and pump or combination "vacuum generator") are remote from toilet and large; can be hard to find space for them below decks on some boats, which can make access for maintenance and repair a problem
- Suction splatters waste all over the inside of the hoses, increasing potential for odor permeation unless thoroughly rinsed out daily
- Only available from "authorized VacuFlush dealers," rarely if ever at a discount

The only manual **vacuum** toilet is the Blake Lavac, made in the UK, but sold in the U.S. After use, the lid is closed, forming a seal. A separate manual diaphragm pump, typically a Henderson, is used to pull in sea water and set up a vacuum in the bowl...when the pedal is depressed the sewage is sucked out. Rebuilding the pump about every 5 years is the only maintenance needed, which makes it especially popular among passage-making sailors An electric version that replaces the manual diaphragm pump with an electric diaphragm pump is also available.

Advantages:
- Exceptional reliability and durability
- Lowest maintenance of any manual toilet

Disadvantages:
- Very Intimidating to children and landlubber guests

OTHER TOILETS
GRAVITY TOLIETS

A **gravity toilet** is actually an RV toilet, and is exactly what the name implies—the bowl has a trapdoor in the bottom through which the bowl is emptied by gravity. As a result gravity toilets can only be used where it's possible to position the toilet directly above a holding tank, which makes their use rare except on houseboats and other large power boats that have holding tanks installed in deep bilges directly beneath the toilet. Although gravity toilets use very little water, they do require pressurized water.

Advantages:
- Uses very little flush water which conserves fresh water and holding tank capacity
- Needs no electric power
- Has no moving parts except the flush pedal, so requires no maintenance
- Has a china bowl on a pedestal that makes it look like a household toilet
- Lower price than most marine toilets

Disadvantages:
- Can only be used if mounted directly above holding tank
- Odor from tank can escape through bowl when trap door is opened

RECIRCULATING TOILETS

Although they've never been widely used in the marine industry, during the 1970s a few manufacturers-Monogram, Danforth and Thetford-produced **re-circulating toilets**, and few still survive to occasionally show up on older boats. Some boat builders in the late '70s and early '80s also created recirculating systems using compact manual toilets and small holding tanks. The Monogram Monomatic and the Danforth Automatic Toilet were CG Certified Type I MSDs (treatment devices) that required the use of chemicals only available from the manufacturer. However, both were discontinued so long ago that neither any parts nor the required chemicals are still available for any of them, invalidating their use as treatment devices. Recirculating toilets do just what the name implies-they recirculate an initial "charge" of water and chemical along with new sewage till the system is full. They hold only 5 gallons—2-3 of which is the initial "charge-and odor control is all but impossible unless emptied every 24 hours. Thetford re-introduced a new version a few years ago that is not a Coast Guard certified treatment device; they are the only manufacturer currently offering a recirculating toilet. Although a recirculating toilet is one solution at a campsite where no running water, sewer or septic are available, a portapotty is less expensive, holds more flushes, and doesn't make you view your waste mixed with flush water in the bowl.

COMPOSTING, DESICCATING, AND INCINERATING TOILETS

Because **composting toilets** are completely self-contained units that do not discharge, they are automatically Coast Guard Certified Type III MSDs. However, as great a solution as composting can be on land, they have very limited application on boats.

First there's the matter of size. The only true composting toilets that work as advertised are too big to fit in 99% of heads. There are ongoing attempts to make smaller self-contained units, but it's just about impossible because there has to be enough room in the drum to "fluff" the contents so it gets enough aeration-otherwise it just rots...and stinks. So while composting can be a wonderful solution in on-land situations where there's no running water or sewer and septic is impossible, but in addition to the size problem, there are also other issues onboard that don't exist in land situations, notably what to do with excess liquids. 90% of human body waste is liquid, not only urine, but solids too, which are about 75% liquid. Liquids must be drained off or you have wet soggy organic material...and wet soggy material doesn't compost, it sits and rots...and stinks! So it's necessary to add dry material (peat moss is the recommended material because it breaks down quickly), which helps some, but not enough, usually leaving more liquids than the evaporator can handle. Excess liquids cannot legally be drained overboard inside the "3 mile limit," so they have to go into a holding tank...and there goes any advantage to installing a composter even if you have room in the head for it. And there are other issues: peat moss storage, a 3" vent stack, and power to run both the evaporator and maintain a controlled temperature well above 70° F; bacterial activity necessary to break down and compost the waste becomes too sluggish to be effective below 60° F, and ceases altogether below 40° F. So a true composter isn't a very realistic option on most boats.

However, the AirHead and Natures Head-which are not true composters, but desiccators-have managed to solve the worst of the excess liquids problem by collecting urine and solids separately. But it's still necessary to dry out solid waste, which requires a fan and heat-which use power—along with added dry material and a bacterial "booster." And there are still the same storage, venting, temperature and urine disposal issues that make true composting problematic.

Advantages
- Self-contained, no plumbing required
- No pumpouts or toilet maintenance required
- Because no flush water is added to the mix, the solids container holds many more "flushes" than most other collection systems.

Disadvantages
- Urine jugs cannot legally be poured overboard inside the "3 mile limit," they must be stored and carried ashore for disposal in toilets or portapotty dump stations.
- Requires power to run blower and heater 24/7/365
- Require bacteria or enzymes to facilitate breakdown of solids
- Requires adding dry material
- Requires storage space for the dry material

Finally, **incinerating toilets**, which also have very limited application on boats. They're really not suitable for boats much smaller than a freighter, and I'm not sure how suitable they are even for freighters! They don't operate on DC, but only on either 220 or 115 volt AC current, so you could only use it if you have a generator or are plugged into shore power. And contrary to popular belief, waste isn't reduced to ash with a brief "whoosh" of heat....the total burn time of at least 60 minutes—up to two hours if subjected to heavy use—at upwards of 600 degrees-and that's not always long enough to completely reduce solids to ash. They need at least a 4" diameter vent stack (chimney) and have components including catalytic converters that require frequent cleaning or the smoke *stinks!* As of this writing, the list price is about $2,000.

Advantages
- Certified as Type III MSD

Disadvantages:
- See above

WHAT SIZE HOLDING TANK DO I NEED?

There really aren't any hard and fast answers to this question. There have been numerous and sometimes arcane attempts to arrive at one, but what it really comes down to 99% of the time is: how much space there is in the boat to put one-or (more often than not) more than one if the boat has two or more heads. The hose run from either head to the tank shouldn't be longer than 6-8'...10' is the absolute maximum. Any longer, and you'll always have waste sitting in the hose to permeate it. So, if the location you've picked means it has to be longer, find another location for the tank that's closer to the head. If you have two or more heads, it's highly likely that you'll need two tanks...or-unless you're in "no discharge" waters-a Type I or II MSD on the head you use the most and a tank on the other one.

Here's my rule of thumb-and it's based on the size of the boat:
- Under 30': 12-20 gallons.
- 30-35': 20-30 gallons.
- 35-40': at least 30 gallons...
- 40' plus: at least 40 gallons total, more if you have room.

There are just too many variables to do it any other way, different types of toilets use different amounts of flush water and people are different. But the following information may help you decide. Just remember that no one has *ever* complained that his holding tank was too big!

Vacuum toilets and electric macerating toilets that draw off the onboard pressurized fresh water system use the least flush water-1-3 quarts/flush.

Manual toilets can use as much as a gallon/flush if pumped long enough to completely rinse the sewage out of the discharge line. There are ways to cut down on that-rinse out the line once a day instead of pumping enough water through with every single flush and other ways that are discussed in the chapter "*Flush With Success*," but the average will still be at least half a gallon, whether the toilet has a piston/cylinder pump or a diaphragm pump.

Electric macerating toilets that have integral raw water intake pumps typically shouldn't need more than about half a gallon (2 liters) per flush, but older basic models can use considerably more to flush solids because there's no way to switch to "dry bowl" without frying the impeller in the intake pump. A couple of brands/models have separate pumps using separate motors, which cuts the water consumption considerably, but you still have to run enough water through it to clear everything out of the macerator, pump and discharge hose unless you want to deal with clogs. However, the further the tank is from the head, the longer any toilet has to be flushed to move the bowl contents from the head to the tank; there are workarounds that help, though.

Those are the parameters for the toilets. Now we need to factor in people: The average adult uses the toilet 5 times in 24 hours. Women—especially older women—need to urinate more often (women also seem to be genetically wired to use about 5x the toilet paper that men do, but that's another issue). Children tend to fall somewhere in between women and men. The average urine "deposit" from an adult is about a cupful (6-8 oz.)...somewhat less for children, depending on their ages because their bladders are like the rest of their bodies—smaller; they grow as the child grows. Some people drink more liquids than others...some sweat more of it out than they process through their kidneys...and that can vary with the time of year.

To find out how many gallons of toilet waste are likely to be generated on your boat per day, keep track of how many times each of you has to use the toilet each day...multiply that by the average volume...then by the amount of flush water your toilet needs, add at least one flush/person/day for solids too (double the flush water volume for that) and you'll come out with the same answer I always do: it's totally impossible to find enough space-at least space you're willing to sacrifice for tankage-for a tank on your boat that will last 4 people a week without a pumpout-and it's highly likely that even two people will fill it in 4-5 days-unless the lee rail gets a *lot* more use than the toilet.

So we're back to my "rule of thumb"...or smaller if there isn't even that much room. But the good news is, you aren't limited to only the few rectangular tanks shown in the marine retail catalogs. There is a company, Ronco Plastics, that makes *top* quality, thick-walled roto-molded tanks, and have more than 400 shapes and sizes-over 100 of which are non-rectangular-to choose from, and for a *very* reasonable price. And, unlike buying an "off the shelf" tank that already has fittings installed, when you order a tank from Ronco, you get to spec your own fittings, sizes and locations, to be installed by them when the tank is made. See *Appendix B* for a link to their marine tank catalog and contact information.

INSTALLING A NEW TOILET AND HOLDING TANK

THE BASICS

STEP 1. Read the chapters *"The Best Toilet For My Boat," "What Size Holding Tank Do I Need?"* and *"Holding Tank Odor—Odor Out the Vent"*

STEP 2. Plan the entire job completely and ask all your questions before you buy anything. (This won't be the only time you'll read that sentence in this book!)

STEP 3. Unless the boat already has one, or you're installing a toilet designed to use pressurized flush water, have your boat hauled to install a 3/4" flush water inlet through-hull and seacock below the waterline. It should be conveniently located next to the toilet so that there is no excuse not to keep the seacock closed except when the head is actually in use. If you're in coastal waters that offer immediate access to open sea beyond the "3 mile limit" and want the ability to dump the tank at sea, it may also be necessary to install a second 1.5" or 1" (depending upon which overboard discharge pump you choose) through-hull and seacock below the waterline.

STEP 4. Measure the space in your head compartment before selecting a toilet. Make sure that wherever you have to mount it offers adequate clearance for both the front and the back of the bowl, room in front of the bowl for your knees when you sit on it, and enough side to side room for the pump.

STEP 5. Find a location for the tank within 6-8' of the toilet that will give you a relatively straight run from the toilet to the tank. If it must be much further from the toilet, plumbing that provides an assist from gravity may be called for. The fewer bends and loops, the less potential for clogs.

STEP 6. Drill two more holes in your boat above the waterline-one in in the side deck for the pump-out fitting that's as close to directly above the tank as possible, the other in the side of the hull for the tank vent. Although 5/8" is the "standard" size for all tank vent lines, 1" is the ideal diameter for waste tank vent lines. The vent thru-hull needs to be high enough on the hull to remain above the waterline at any angle of heel.

STEP 7. Measure your hose lengths...add at least 2 more feet than you think you'll need.

STEP 8. Read the chapter *"Sanitation Hoses and Hose fittings."* It explains how to put hoses on fittings and the right way to install threaded fittings into a tank.

STEP 9. Go shopping for a tank, hoses, fittings, enough hose clamps to double clamp all connections, a pump-out deck fitting, a through-hull fitting for the tank vent, a ¾" vented loop, a toilet, some teflon tape, and bedding compound. If you plan to be able to flush the toilet directly overboard, you'll also need a 1.5" diverter valve (commonly called a "Y-valve") and a 1.5" vented loop.

STEP 10: Now that you've bought everything, read the installation instructions for all of it, and make sure you understand all of them completely before beginning any work!! One more time: It's always easier and less expensive to do anything right the first time than it is to do it over.

STEP 11. Recruit help that's knowledgeable and experienced when it comes to putting holes in your boat and installing any wiring needed for an electric toilet. An electric toilet should always be on its own separate dedicated circuit, shared by nothing—not even cabin lights-that can reduce power to the toilet, because low voltage is highly destructive to electric motors.

Be sure to follow all instructions for wire sizes which can vary depending upon distance from the battery.

STEP 12. Set aside an entire weekend-after you've installed the intake fitting and seacock-to do the job.

INSTALLING A BELOW-WATERLINE TOILET DESIGNED TO USE RAW WATER

("Raw" water is the sea/lake/river/bay water your boat is floating in, pulled into the toilet by the toilet's pump). If any part of the toilet will be below the boat's waterline, it's necessary to install a vented loop (anti-siphon device) in the toilet intake that's at least 8-12" above the waterline at any angle of heel, which, on most sailboats puts it 2-3 feet above the bowl. Why? Because water outside the boat will try to seek its own level inside the boat, and relying on the "dry"/"flush" valve to keep it out is a good way to sink your boat—or, if you're lucky, only have to mop up a lot of water. Wet/dry valves fail, and people—especially landlubber guests-fail even more often to remember to leave the valve in the "dry" position. A vented loop not only provides a siphon break, but it also puts an arch in the hose higher than the waterline. However, the intake vented loop does not belong in the flush water intake line between the thru-hull and pump because it pulls in air to break a siphon that would interfere with the toilet's ability to prime. So the intake vented loop has to go between the pump and the bowl, which requires replacing the short piece of hose the manufacturer used to connect them with longer hose.

However, if the toilet is an electric model that does not have a connecting hose between the pump and the bowl, you'll have no choice but to put the vented loop in the line from the thru-hull to the pump. In that case, it's necessary to replace the air valve in the vented loop with an electric solenoid valve wired to the flush button. The solenoid closes the air valve to let the toilet prime when the flush button is pushed, opens it again to break the flow of water when the flush button is released. As of this writing, Jabsco is the only source for this particular solenoid valve. For decades the part number for this valve was 37068-000, now replaced by a new version, part number 37068-2000. Jabsco specifies this one as being specifically for the 37010 series toilet, but it will work with any toilet that has an integrated intake/discharge motor operated by a single push button. The obsolete valve is still on a lot of shelves as of this writing.

If the toilet is to be installed to flush directly overboard at sea beyond the "3 mile limit" or through a Type I or II MSD that discharges overboard, there must also be a vented loop in the toilet discharge line.

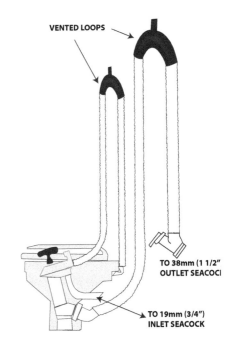

VENTED LOOPS

TO 38mm (1 1/2")
OUTLET SEACOCK

TO 19mm (3/4")
INLET SEACOCK

The best place to put vented loops on most boats is immediately after the toilet, mounted on the bulkhead behind the toilet. If the toilet came with a straight discharge fitting, call the manufacturer to request a 90 degree discharge fitting. Aim the discharge hose straight up, go over the loop and back down to an inline 90 degree fitting...then on to the rest of the installation.

Vented loops do not require vent lines. Instead, there is-or should be-an air valve in the vented loop that only allows air *into* the line to break a siphon and does not allow anything to squirt out. Bronze and more expensive PVC vented loops may have a "cap" type air valve. However, if you have a typical PVC vented loop, look closely at the hole in the nipple on the top of the loop; you'll see that it's threaded. That's where the air valve goes. But because air valves are replaceable parts, they're often sold separately. So owners who aren't knowledgeable about vented loops don't know they need one. In fact, it's actually a very bad idea to put a vent line on a vented loop because the diameter has to be so small-only 1/4"-that it quickly becomes clogged with sea water minerals and salt, turning the vented loop into an unvented loop that no longer has any ability to break a siphon.

Vented loop with
solenoid valve
Photo courtesy of Jabsco

Air valves do require a little maintenance—periodic cleaning to remove any buildup of waste, salt and/or sea water minerals, and occasional replacement.
So they're almost always sold separately. The teenager working in the marine store doesn't even know they exist, so you may have to order one...which is why people put vent lines on vented loops. But because it's solved the problem-no more squirting-it's 'out of sight, out of mind' and so never cleaned or replaced.

INSTALLING THE TANK

Almost all tank manufacturers recommend supporting a tank on all sides to protect the tank walls from any damage that can be caused by the weight of the contents (water and waste weigh 8.333 lbs./gallon). If the tank walls are less than .25" thick, it's essential that you do this. However, top quality tanks with walls that are at least 5/16" thick, increasing with the size of the tank, are usually strong enough to support the contents without bulging. Unless your plans include being tossed around in the Southern Ocean or similar conditions (possible but unlikely) it's really only necessary to secure the tank to prevent it from sliding than it is to preventing it from bouncing. This can be done by framing the corners of the tank with quarter round or picture frame moulding, or strapping it down with tie-downs (easy to make using lawn chair webbing and grommets).

U.S. Coast Guard regulations require some means of determining and warning the owner/users when a waste (black water or gray water) tank is at least 75% full. If the tank is easily accessed to check contents level visually, that's enough to satisfy the requirements of the regulation. But if the tank is not in a location that makes it easy to check the contents level, or is made of a material that makes visual inspection impossible, a tank level indicator must be installed. The best tank level indicators are no longer those that have probes ("senders") inside the tank that quickly become clogged by the animal fats in a waste; they use senders that attach to outside walls of the tank, never coming in contact with the contents. These can be used on any material except metal. See *Appendix A* for my brand recommendations.

IF THE TANK IS TO BE DISCHARGED OVERBOARD

The tank discharge hose must be split with a diverter valve (commonly called a "Y-valve") installed...one side going to the deck pump-out fitting, additional hose from the other side going to a pump and then to a below-waterline thru-hull. If the pump were installed directly inline with the deck pump-out fitting, it would block the path from the pump-out fitting to the tank. Many production boat builders only install a tee or wye fitting in the tank discharge line, not because it's a good idea, but because they're cheaper than "Y-valves." In fact, it's a very bad idea. A "Y-valve" installed between the tank and the macerator is both a "fail-safe" backup to the seacock, and can shut off the flow of tank contents in the event the macerator needs repair when the tank is full. Or better yet, eliminate the y-valve by specifying two discharge fittings when you order the tank—one that goes directly to the deck pump-out fitting, the other going directly to the overboard discharge pump and thru-hull. Use a shutoff valve instead of a standard thread-to barb tank fitting to connect the overboard discharge line.

Bosworth Y Valve
Photo courtesy of Bosworth Co.

There are three types of overboard discharge pumps: manual diaphragm, electric diaphragm and electric impeller pumps.

Bosworth Guzzler
Photo courtesy of Bosworth

Jabsco Macerator
Photo courtesy of Jabsco

SeaLand T Series Pump
Photo courtesy of Dometic

Diaphragm pumps get their names from the flexible rubber bag-like "diaphragm" that stretches across one side of a housing. A human moves a handle in a manual diaphragm pump back and forth to pull the walls of the diaphragm apart , and push them back together, pulling water or waste in one side of the pump as it pulls the walls of the diaphragm apart in an "upstroke," and pushing the contents out the other side with the "downstroke" that pushes the walls of the diaphragm back together. Check valves to keep things moving the right direction. Electric diaphragm pumps work the same way, but have an internal mechanism that does the pumping. Manual and electric diaphragm pumps are not macerating pumps.

An impeller macerator pump has a neoprene rubber device installed called an impeller that pulls ("impels") holding tank contents through the pump. A macerator blade that's similar to the blade in a blender "purees" any solid waste and/or toilet paper that haven't dissolved. A macerator pump should be installed close to the tank discharge (but never connected directly to the tank) to allow it to prime quickly. The longer the impeller has to run dry, the more friction heat takes its toll on it. It should also be easily accessible for maintenance and repair -another reason to install a shutoff valve in the tank discharge port, because overboard discharge pumps never need maintenance or repair when a tank is empty! The macerator pump switch should be in a location that allows monitoring of the dumping progress to prevent the macerator from running dry and to make sure the tank is actually emptying (see the chapter on tank vent maintenance).

An electric diaphragm pump costs a bit more than an impeller macerator pump, but can be located almost anywhere that's convenient (within the manufacturer's specified limits)—even above the tank—because, unlike impeller pumps, diaphragm pumps can run dry without harm. And—also unlike impeller macerator pumps, electric diaphragm pumps typically require little or no maintenance or repair.

Owners of sailboats and smaller power boats with limited electrical resources may choose to install a manual diaphragm pump instead of an electric macerator or diaphragm pump. I leave that choice up to you.

If the tank is to be discharged below the waterline (and I do hope it is!) it's necessary to install a vented loop between the overboard discharge pump and the through-hull that's at least 8-12" above the waterline at any angle of heel. The seacock should be kept closed at all times except when actually dumping the tank, but standards call for a vented loop nonetheless.

REPLACING AN EXISTING TOILET

Marine toilets aren't like the ones at home; those don't have any moving parts to wear out, marine toilets do—and not just the parts in "rebuild" or "service" kits, but the hardware too. Pump housings and impeller housings wear and get scratched, even break. Everything has a lifespan and marine toilets are no exception! The average life of a compact manual marine toilet is 2-3 years for the least expensive, 7-9 years for higher quality. "Standard size" manual marine toilets can have working lives of up to 20 years, but only if they're always kept well lubricated and rebuilt every 5-6 years. Manufacturers are also fond of redesigning toilets, and the new versions always require at least some parts that are different from the previous versions. It's not profitable for manufacturers to support obsolete discontinued equipment forever, and they don't. 10 years is about the maximum length of time parts remain available for any discontinued equipment. So sooner or later the time has to come when there's really only one thing to do with an old marine toilet: give it a decent burial and replace it!

So the first step: Finally admit that and read the chapter "*The Best Toilet For My Boat.*" Settle on the type of toilet you want, do a little research to find out which makes/models most people recommend—this is the time to ask lots of questions-and go shopping for the best price on the one you choose.

Now that you've bought it, it's time to get to work.

Every time the subject of replacing the toilet comes up in a discussion, the first two questions invariably are, "How do I access the nuts on the mounting bolts to remove the toilet?" and "Will the existing mounting bolt holes match the bolt pattern on the new toilet?"

The answer to the first question is: All marine toilets are mounted using lag bolts that have no nuts, so you only need to back them out.

The answer to the second question is: Unless you're replacing your toilet with the exact same model from the exact same manufacturer, not a chance. And even if you are, like car manufacturers, marine products manufacturers like to re-style and "improve" their latest models, so even a new version of the same make/model toilet is likely to have new mounting bolt patterns and hose routing that's different from previous models. At least one hole will be re-useable—and maybe even two-but I recommend filling them all, then re-tapping to make sure the new bolts will fit tightly. You don't want a wobbly new toilet! Drilling new mounting bolt holes and filling the ones that don't match is not a major project, honest!

On land, thanks to the National Plumbing Code, you can replace any brand toilet with any other brand toilet and they'll all fit and work properly. That is not true of marine toilets! So when choosing a new toilet, it's essential that you measure!! Not only side to side, but front to back, especially if you're upgrading from a small "marine" toilet bowl to the larger "household" size. The discharge hole in a marine toilet bowl is dead center in the middle of the bowl. So if the bowl is bigger, it will not only need more room in front and on each side, it will need more room behind it...the whole toilet may have to be moved forward. That can be a problem (not necessarily insurmountable, though) if the toilet is on a "ledge."

When replacing electric toilets, wire gauge, switching and fusing is also an important consideration, because they must be keyed to the power requirements, wire sizes etc. of the new toilet. Those may not necessarily be the same as those for the old toilet. So it's very important to check all the specs for the new toilet and to determine whether your existing electrical components are a good match.

In summary: When replacing an old marine toilet with a new one, be prepared to deal with drilling new mounting bolt holes and plugging old ones, re-routing or replacing hoses, and if you're replacing an electric toilet, replacing all the wiring with those that meet the requirements for the new toilet.

When installing or replacing a system all connections should be double-clamped. Only materials rated for marine sanitation should ever be used, and any below-waterline through-hull should include a seacock that is easily accessible by the boat owner. Only toilets that are designed to use pressurized water should ever be connected to the onboard fresh water system. If any part of the system is below the waterline, anti-siphon devices (vented loops) must be installed in both the discharge and toilet intake. Toilets and holding tanks that discharge overboard should only do so below waterline.

SANITATION HOSES AND HOSE FITTINGS

Because hose wall-thickness varies, hose sizes always refer to the Inner Diameter (ID). For the same reason, fittings sizes always refer to the Outer Diameter (OD). This guarantees that a 1" hose will be the right size to fit onto a 1" fitting.

-HOSES-

Quality

Use only flexible smooth walled rubber or flexible PVC that is rated specifically for marine sanitation use. Although white hot tub hose looks like the same white hose marine stores sell for more than twice the price, it is not the same hose. Hot tub hose is rated to carry water only; sewage odor will permeate it in a heartbeat. Same is true if you try to use nylon water hose for a vent line (something boat builders often do to save a little money). In no time, there you'll be with a stinky boat again and a second bill for the hose you should have bought in the first place, not to mention all that wasted blood, sweat, and tears you shed installing it. Since we all agree that odor, especially sewage odors, do more to ruin a day on the water, let's all agree too that sanitation hose is not the place to go cheap. Buy the top rated hoses (notice I said "top rated," not "most expensive") hose for every part of the system—toilet discharge and flush water inlet, tank discharge to deck pump-out fitting and any overboard discharge pump and thru-hull, tank vent line-if you only want to do this job once.

Sizes

Most marine toilets, manual and electric, need a 1.5" hose. For decades all Jabsco toilets had a 1" discharge that needed 1" hose. They now offer toilet discharge fittings that fit both 1" and 1.5" hose. Flush water inlet hose is ¾" for toilets that use "raw" (sea, lake, river) water, ½" for toilets designed to use pressurized fresh water. Although most toilets are shipped with a straight discharge fitting, most, if not all, also offer a 90 degree discharge fitting that can be yours just for the asking. Ask for one if the hose coming from a straight fitting will be stressed by a route that has to go to one side or the other.

HOLDING TANKS

The standard size inlet or "fill" fitting on all tanks—water, fuel and waste-is 1.5". If the toilet is discharge hose is only 1", an adapter fitting may be required. However replacing the toilet discharge fitting and hose with a 1.5" hose and fitting is a better option. The standard size tank vent hose on all tanks—water, fuel and waste—is 5/8". And while that's big enough to provide adequate venting for water and fuel tanks, 1" is the ideal size for a holding tank vent line on most boats, even larger on bigger boats. The standard size pump-out/discharge hose is also 1.5".

part III

FLUSH WITH SUCCESS!

Before most of us had reached the ripe old age of three, we thought our "potty training" was finished...then we grew up and bought boats. Would you believe that most equipment failures in marine sanitation systems happen because the boat owner didn't take the time to find out—or explain to guests-how that particular make/model toilet works, how to flush it correctly or, least of all, how to maintain it?

Most new boat owners fail to realize that the only thing the toilet on the boat has in common with the toilet at home is the same intended use, and a porcelain bowl. The toilet at home has no moving parts...flush water is supplied to a tank that has a flapper valve (plug) in the bottom of it that's attached to a chain. The flush lever pulls the plug, allowing the water in the tank to flood the bowl and start a siphon that pulls the bowl contents up and over a loop ("trapway") and on to the sewer pipe. It couldn't be simpler, requires no maintenance.

But a marine toilet is a working piece of machinery with moving parts—a manual pump is full of gaskets, seals, o-rings, valves, etc. Electric toilets have motors, impellers, doodads called "macerators" that are essentially the same thing as the blades in a blender and solenoids in addition to a few of the same seals and valves etc. And all those moving parts not only require at least some maintenance but an understanding of how marine toilets work and how to flush them. The toilet at home is also just an appliance; once the flush leaves the bowl, it's on its way to the sewer, out of your life. But the toilet on a boat—in fact, every piece of equipment on a boat—is just one component in a system, and everything that happens in any one part of that system impacts the whole system! Not realizing that bowl contents move through the system only as long as people continue flushing, and also overly fearful of filling up holding tanks with flush water, people stop flushing the second the bowl is empty, leaving bits of paper and solids trapped in the pump, macerator, and/or sitting in the discharge line to permeate the hose, or worse yet, lead to a clog. As for preventive maintenance, when it comes to toilets, the idea has never entered most people's minds..."fix what breaks" is all that ever occurs to them.

In this chapter, we'll talk about how marine toilets work and how to flush them correctly; we'll talk about maintaining them in another chapter.

MANUAL TOILETS

Most manual marine toilets have piston/cylinder pumps that all work pretty much the same way: a piston rod inside a cylinder pulls water in on one stroke and pushes it out on the other stroke. Manual toilets are "double-action," that is both sides of the piston (or diaphragm) are used simultaneously for different purposes. Beginning with the operating handle or knob in the down position, when you pull it up, a vacuum is created in the space below the piston which pulls some of the contents from the toilet bowl and into the bottom half of the pump cylinder. Then, when you push it down, a pair of built-in valves reverses and the material is pushed out of the bottom half of the pump and downstream – to a holding tank, treatment system, or overboard (where legal). A lever or knob on the top of the toilet pump operates a valve in the intake that opens the path to the intake hose in the "wet" or "flush" position, closes the intake to block the flow of flush water coming into the bowl in the "dry" position. In the "wet" mode, the pump pulls water in *and* pushes bowl contents and flush water out. Most people use the "dry" mode primarily for only two purposes: 1) to clear the bowl to keep water from sloshing out when on a hard heel or when encountering rough seas. 2) To aid in clearing a temporary clog, such as too much toilet paper, etc. It won't bring in any outside water so there's no risk of overflowing the bowl. But there's a very valuable third use for the dry mode: to push the flush to the tank without also filling up the tank with flush water. Few people realize that air pressure created by pumping a manual toilet that is in good condition can move waste and water through the system up to about 6 linear feet or 4 vertical feet without bringing in any flush water. Switch back to the "wet mode" for a couple of pumps to bring in water to rinse the pump and discharge line, then switch back to dry to pump that through to the tank.

The Raritan "Fresh Head" has a diaphragm pump beside the bowl instead of a piston/cylinder pump, but the operating principles are the same – the two sides of the diaphragm are utilized to perform two different functions at the same time (rinse water in – dirty water out).

MANUAL TOILETS—FLUSHING 101

Unless the system is plumbed to provide help from gravity, bowl contents only move through the system as long as you keep pumping. So find out how many pump strokes it takes to push the bowl contents all the way to their destination—holding tank, MSD, or the through-hull (when at sea)—and religiously pump it that many times plus two or three more to rinse the hose. Nothing left in the system means nothing to build up and clog the system...*and* no standing sewage in the discharge hose means less likelihood of the hose becoming permeated with odor.

"But I don't want to fill up my holding tank with flush water!" you cry. Then learn to use the dry mode to do more than just move the last bit of water out of the bowl! Switch back to "wet" or "flush" and pump only enough times to bring in enough water to rinse the bowl and the hoses, then switch back to dry to pump that through to the tank or thru-hull.

And then, once a day-last thing before you go to bed is a good time, because that's when the system is likely to be unused for the longest period of time-close the intake seacock, flush the toilet as dry as possible, and flush a couple of quarts of fresh water-use a cup from the sink-through the system, (VacuFlush owners fill the bowl to the rim and flush). It's especially important to do that last thing before the boat will sit, even just till next weekend.

Since no manual marine toilet except the Raritan Fresh Head is designed to bring in water and hold it in the bowl, use a cup to put at least a pint of water from the sink in the bowl before depositing solids (this also keeps the bowl cleaner). Then make sure to flush the bowl contents all the way through the system.

A marine toilet can't "swallow" as much at one time as a household toilet, so be sparing with toilet paper and when circumstances make it advisable, flush early and often.

ELECTRIC TOILETS

Two types of electric macerating toilets are available: those that have an intake pump that draws in "raw water" (sea/lake/river water) and those that are designed to flush with pressurized water. Raw water models may have an integral intake pump or a remote intake pump. Models that have an integral intake pump-.i.e. mounted at the back of the motor—do not have a "dry" flush mode. Most intake pumps have a hard rubber gizmo in them called an impeller because it impels (pulls) water through it using centrifugal power; the Raritan SeaEra has a diaphragm intake pump. The same motor that operates the discharge pump and macerator also spins the impeller shaft. If the impeller spins dry—without any water to lubricate it-dry friction heat "fries" the edges of the impeller vanes, preventing it from priming, destroying the impeller. So the intake seacock must always be open and flush water coming in while the toilet is being flushed. This makes closing the intake seacock and using the shower head to add water to the bowl a very bad idea!

Electric toilets designed to use pressurized flush water from the boat's fresh water system do not have an intake pump. A valve that acts the same way as a faucet—it opens and closes to allow and stop the flow of water-is used to connect the toilet intake line to the cold water line in the head. This valve may or may not be an electric solenoid valve (different from the solenoid valve used in anti-siphon devices; see the chapter "Installing a New Toilet and Holding Tank").

Some models which have remote sea water pumps and those designed to use pressurized water may or may not have a "dry" mode. Some may allow water to be added to the bowl ahead of use; if not, use a cup from the sink to add water ahead of solids.

(Important note: It is safe to connect any toilet that's designed by the manufacturer to flush using pressurized fresh to the boat's potable water supply. However, no "raw water" flush toilet, manual or electric, should ever be connected to the onboard fresh water system. Doing so can pollute the fresh water supply or damage the toilet or both.)

ELECTRIC TOILETS 101

Read the directions for operating your toilet *before* operating it. If a previous owner didn't keep the manual, get one from the manufacturer. Most are available for download from the manufacturer's website. However, if no manual is available, or if the toilet is not equipped with a timed flush, as a general rule it's necessary to keep your finger on the button for a minimum of 3 full seconds after urination, and at least 10 seconds after solids.

Electric toilets can't handle as much volume at once as a household toilet either, as marine toilet passages are smaller than at home *(see Manual Toilets – Flushing 101)*, so it's also necessary to be sparing with toilet paper and flush more than once when circumstances warrant it. Often, when toilet paper clogs in the "throat" at the bottom of the bowl, it's due to too little water in the bowl or the paper hasn't had time to soak enough water to start to dissolve. Stop flushing, add water to the bowl with a cup and wait for 60 seconds or so, then try again. It'll usually go down the second time. If it doesn't, wait an hour for solids to begin dissolving and try again.

VACUFLUSH TOILETS

The VacuFlush toilet is a three component system-the bowl assembly, the vacuum accumulator tank (not to be confused with a holding tank) and a vacuum pump. The vacuum tank and vacuum pump may be a combined gizmo called the "vacuum generator," that includes both and works the same way as separate vacuum tank and pump. And that's *all* there is to the VacuFlush toilet. The holding tank is *not* part of the VacuFlush toilet system...nor is the overboard discharge pump to dump the tank, nor is any vent line filter. Dometic Sanitation (formerly SeaLand Technology) does offer "packages" that add all or some of those things to the toilet system, but it's important to understand, especially when it comes to troubleshooting it, only the aforementioned three components are part of the toilet.

The vacuum pump has *two* functions: it suctions the air out of the plumbing between the toilet bowl and itself while simultaneously pushing the flush the rest of the way to the tank, treatment device or thru-hull. The vacuum tank has a switch and a sensor on it that starts the vacuum pump when there's a loss of "vacuum" (toilet is flushed or an air leak in the system) and turns it off when the correct amount of negative pressure has been reached. How long it runs after the pedal has been released depends on the distance from the pump to the bowl...the shorter the distance, the shorter pump run time. The accumulated "vacuum" only pulls the bowl contents *to* the pump; the pump has to push it the rest of the way.

When flushing a VacuFlush, *don't* just "pop" the pedal-whooosh, it's gone-and back up. That pedal also starts the flush water...leave it down long enough to rinse the bowl contents out of the system...then let the pedal snap back up. It's spring loaded for a reason: letting it snap insures that the dome in the bowl seals completely. And it's also a good idea to keep the pedal down or your finger on the flush button available on some newer VacuFlush models for a minimum of 3 full seconds after urination, and at least 10 seconds after solids to rinse out the pump.

A FEW WORDS ABOUT TOILET PAPER

Some boat owners insist that "nothing goes into the toilet unless you've eaten it first." That's not bad advice, but it's not necessary to be that strict; any marine toilet can swallow limited amounts of quick-dissolve toilet paper too, but nothing else—no paper towels, no condoms or tampons, not even facial tissue and especially *no wet wipes*!!!

Marine toilets, unlike household toilets, are working machinery. And today, unlike years past when waste was flushed directly overboard, marine toilets are no longer "stand alone" appliances, but only one component of a complete system. They don't require a lot of maintenance, and rarely need repair except when preventive maintenance is neglected—which it is, all too often. I've never quite understood why people who'd never dream of waiting till the engine starts smoking to change the oil would rather take a toilet apart when the bowl is full and it won't go down than spend 15-30 minutes once a year on preventive maintenance when it's clean and dry. Nor does it make any sense to me that people who'd never dream of just adding a little oil to the engine when it starts to smoke think that's the way to keep a toilet properly lubricated.

Marine toilets have seals and valves and other parts that wear, and as they wear the toilet becomes less and less efficient. You don't notice it because it's gradual. You don't notice your spouse getting older day by day either—because you see him every day. But you notice how much your mother has aged if you haven't seen her for a while. And you notice that "Jack's" new toilet sure works a lot better than your old one. You also notice when yours begins to develop problems—leaks, squeaks, or quits working altogether—which, unless the toilet is abused, isn't likely to happen without giving you plenty of warning.

Why does it happen? When boats sit for weeks or even days, the seals and valves dry out and stick to the inside of their housings; dried salt makes them stick even better and also is abrasive, so pumping a manual toilet without adequate lubrication wears the seals and scratches the inside of the pump cylinder. The first flush of an electric toilet or use of a macerator pump after sitting for several days can put enough strain on an impeller to crack a vane. Friction heat from running dry, even momentarily, each time the pump has be primed wears a microscopic amount off the edges of any impeller, gradually, reducing its efficiency a little more each time. Dry rubber and neoprene—especially if it's salt encrusted, scratches the housing. Even with constant live-aboard use, over time both seals and pump cylinders wear, and because it's people, not a precise machine, who pump manual heads, they wear unevenly. The best cure is prevention, so lubricate your toilet annually, rebuild it—that is, install a kit that replaces all the seals, valves, impellers etc.—every 3-5 years (the better quality the toilet and the better it's kept lubricated, the less often it should need rebuilding). And don't put anything down it except waste and limited amounts of the right kind of toilet paper

The alternative? You too can join the group complaining about what a nasty job unclogging the toilet is!

LUBRICATING A MANUAL TOILET

Many people just wait till the toilet starts to squeak and become hard to pump, then pour some mineral oil or vegetable oil down it. That's ok in an emergency, till you can get home and do it right, but it's not the way to maintain the toilet. Not only is this very hard on the toilet, but it's a never-ending job because anything poured down the toilet washes out in just a few flushes. That wasn't always true. All the parts in marine toilets that are now made of rubber and neoprene were originally made of leather. Leather soaks up oil, so keeping a toilet lubricated by pouring oil down the toilet when it could sit in the pump long enough for the leathers to soak it up a few times a year worked just fine. But rubber and neoprene don't soak up oil or anything else, so any "lubricant" flushed down the toilet is quickly washed out. Continuing to use the toilet as it gets harder and harder to pump and/or starts to squeak is the worst thing you can do!

Why is that so hard on the toilet? Because a toilet doesn't squeak unless it needs lubrication; that squeaking is the sound of rubber rubbing against the inside of the pump cylinder, being worn away. Waiting till it squeaks to lubricate it is like waiting till an engine starts to smoke to add oil.

Remember what I said earlier about a toilet being only one component of a complete system? That anything you do to one component in any system impacts the entire system? Pouring oil down the toilet also creates a surface inside the discharge hose that's a trap for salt and other sea water minerals, and bits of paper and solid waste to build up inside it. And it creates an oil slick on the surface in the holding tank, which—if you read the chapter on holding tank odor—you already know why that increases odor problems. Finally, anything flushed down a toilet except body waste, toilet paper and products approved by the device manufacturer has the potential to damage a Type I or II treatment device.

Ever wondered why a new toilet doesn't need any lubrication for at least a year? It's because every toilet leaves the factory slathered with thick Teflon or silicon grease that takes a full season or even longer to be flushed out. Replacing it just once or twice a year is all it takes to keep a toilet pumping smoothly. And it's only a 15 minute job!

On some makes/models it may be possible to take the top off the pump. If not, it's a simple matter—removing 3 or 4 bolts—to lift the pump off the base.

1. Buy a tube of SuperLube or similar thick Teflon or silicon grease...thick grease, not a liquid or a spray
2. Close the intake seacock. Do not disconnect any hoses
3. Take the pump off the base (only requires removing 4 screws or bolts)
4. Stick the tube nozzle into the pump and put a healthy squirt—a tablespoon or more-of grease into it
5. Put the toilet back onto the base, tighten the screws/bolts—but not too tight, or you can crack the housing
6. Pump the toilet a few times to spread it all over the inside of the pump cylinder and you're done..."good to go" for the entire season

And, by keeping the pump lubricated this way, you extend the life of the seals and valves, reducing the need for rebuilds. The best time to lubricate a toilet is in the fall, as part of winterizing. The grease protects the rubber parts in the toilet from drying out, which also extends their life.

A FEW WORDS ABOUT JOKER VALVES
(No, I don't know why it's called a joker valve either)

Joker valves should be replaced annually, no less often than every two years. But I sometimes wonder if there are any boat owners who know what a joker valve actually does. It's the first thing everyone suggests as the cause for every symptom a toilet can develop, even holding tanks that fill up with sea water when the overboard seacock is left open. At least 90% of the people who come to me with any sanitation system problem tell me that they replaced the joker valve but it didn't help.

JOKER VALVES 101

Replacing the joker valve is not a cure for a pump that squeaks or is hard to pump, backpressure when flushing, water rising in the bowl through the toilet intake—or no flush water at all. A joker valve isn't even part of the pump, it's just a one way rubber valve in the toilet discharge line. Most people think that the only thing the joker valve does is acts as a check valve to stop backflow from returning to the toilet or prevent odor from the tank escaping through the toilet And while that is indeed one of the joker valve's functions, it's not a joker valve's most important function...in fact, the joker valve is the single most important replaceable part in a manual toilet. Here's why:

Joker Valve
Photo courtesy
of Raritan Engineering

Here's how the discharge half of the pump works: On the upstroke of the piston, a vacuum is created in the area beneath the piston. This causes the joker valve to close tightly, and the flapper valve beneath the pump to open, allowing some of the contents of the toilet bowl to be drawn into the bottom half of the pump. Then, on the down stroke of the piston, the flapper valve is slammed shut, and the effluent is forced out of the bottom of the pump, through the joker valve, and off down the line. But when the joker valve becomes worn and/or there's a buildup of sea water minerals on it, it can no longer seal tightly on the upstroke of the piston...less vacuum is generated when you pump it. And as it becomes more worn less and less vacuum, till finally the bowl contents simply move up and down a bit, but don't go anywhere.

You probably won't notice the loss of efficiency at first because it's so gradual...same as we don't see that we've gotten a little older than we were yesterday when we look in the mirror each morning. But if it's been two years or longer since you replaced the joker valve, I'd bet real money that you need to pump the toilet at least 50% more times to move the bowl contents to the tank or all the way out the thru-hull....*if* they're even getting there at all any more.

In both manual and electric toilets, the joker valve does have a second function: prevent backflow from flooding the bowl ("flooding" being the operative word; even a brand new joker valve won't prevent slow seepage, at least not for very long) while allowing bowl contents to pass through it going the other way. The flood or seepage is always caused by something else-a blocked holding tank vent or sea water mineral buildup in the hose to the point that it's reduced the diameter enough to restrict flow, or a tank that's full to overflowing, or even gravity if the hose from the toilet to the tank runs uphill...water does insist on running downhill, you know! Replacing the joker valve may slow the rate at which backflow rises in the bowl but it won't cure what's causing the backflow in the first place, and that has to be somewhere downstream of the toilet.

REBUILD A MANUAL TOILET OR REPLACE THE PUMP?

Everything has a lifespan, and eventually even the most scrupulously well-lubricated seals and valves wear out (they wear out a lot faster in neglected toilets). As they wear, the toilet gradually becomes less and less efficient. So the question becomes, do you install a rebuild kit or just replace the toilet?

That depends on the toilet. All marine toilets are not created equal, and in recent years, the trend has been away from durability and toward "disposability"—replace instead of repair. But replace with what? Wilcox-Crittenden is gone, Thetford now only sells Tecma electric macerating toilets. As of this writing there are only two U.S. manufacturers left still build for durability instead of "disposability:" Groco, who makes only two toilets, both manual-the bronze "throne" Model K (to which a motor can be added to replace the pump handle only) and the compact HF—and Raritan Engineering whose PHII has been the top rated manual toilet in its class for several decades and whose complete line of manual and electric macerating toilets are always top rated too. Replacing a $500-$1000 toilet with a $100 toilet because the rebuild kit for it is $85 is tantamount to scrapping a Rolls Royce or a Mercedes and replacing it with a Yugo because a tune-up for the Rolls costs almost as much as the Yugo. But if the whole toilet can be replaced with its own current make/model, or comparable make/model if no longer made, for less than the price of two rebuild kits, the easiest solution is a new toilet of the same or better quality.

My rule of thumb: toilets in the $100-$200 price have an average life-span of 2-5 years; if it needs more than just lubrication and a new joker valve, and a rebuild or "service" kit is close to the same price as a new pump, replace the pump or consider spending a little more for a more durable higher quality toilet. Toilets in the $200-$500 price range can easily last 10-20 years with reasonable maintenance (keep it lubricated, rebuild every 5-6 years); whether to rebuild it or upgrade it depends on its age and how well it's been maintained. Any toilet with a price tag over $500 should last at least 20 years with proper maintenance and is worth whatever it costs to maintain it.

LUBRICATING AN ELECTRIC TOILET

Most electric toilets require very little lubrication—usually only the intake impeller. The motor is sealed, so it requires none. Inspect it every few months for signs of corrosion (which means something is leaking that shouldn't be) and follow manufacturer's recommendations.

REBUILD OR REPLACE AN ELECTRIC TOILET?

Electric toilets need very little maintenance and most are far more durable than manual toilets, because by the time most of them do need maintenance or repair that wasn't due to abuse, there have been a lot of improvements in marine toilet technology. So it usually makes more sense to upgrade to the current version or a better quality toilet instead of putting more money than the price of an impeller into an old obsolete toilet. Most are available as "conversion kits" that allow you to re-use your existing bowl, seat and lid even if you switch brands and models.

MAINTAINING A VACUFLUSH TOILET

VacuFlush toilets require very little preventive maintenance—replace the duckbill valves in the pump if the pump starts to cycle for no reason between flushes or every couple of years (annually if you live aboard) as preventive maintenance. Once a day, flush a full bowl of water through it to rinse out the hoses and the vacuum pump. That's all.

It can develop problems though, often the result of using too little flush water. If only urine is flushed-no water added to the bowl first, no TP either-then yes, you can get away with as little as a pint per flush. But it's essential to add at least half a bowl of water ahead of solids or any TP (in other words, every time a female uses the toilet), and at least once a day you need to run at least half a bowl of clean water through to rinse out the pump and duckbills-to prevent a buildup in the pump or bits of waste or TP from becoming stuck in a duckbill, creating one of those pesky air leaks that causes the pump to cycle for no reason.

But not all problems are caused by "operator error." Fortunately VacuFlush owner's manuals include the most complete troubleshooting guide of any toilet manufacturer; every possible symptom, probable causes and cures is in it. So if you don't have an owners' manual for it, get one. It doesn't matter how old or how new your VacuFlush system is, it's changed so little except cosmetically since Mansfield Plumbing introduced it in 1978 that the trouble-shooting guide for any model year is just as applicable to any other year. Be sure to refer to it before deciding to self-diagnose and treat any problems because the causes and cures to many of them are counter-intuitive, which could cause you to turn one problem into three.

Remember: Preventive maintenance is called that because it prevents problems that will have to be fixed. You get to do preventive maintenance on your terms, when it's convenient for you...unlike repairs, which are never needed at a convenient time!

KEEPING IT CLEAN

Never use bleach, nor any household chemical bowl cleaners, ammonia, Lysol, pine oil cleaners, "antibacterial" cleaners, solvents or anything containing alcohol or any petroleum products in *any* marine toilet. These are not only harmful to rubber, neoprene and Lectra/San electrodes, they break down hoses, causing them to become more susceptible to permeation.

We're partial to Raritan C.P. Cleans Potties!, which is a bio-enzymatic (and therefore works with nature instead of against it) bowl, sump and drain cleaner that cleans without scrubbing, destroys odors on contact, and contains no harmful chemicals that can damage the toilet or negatively impact other parts of the system or the environment. If that's not available, wipe out the bowl with a little Comet or Soft-Scrub on a wet paper towel or sponge. Unless you use way too much, it's ok to flush to rinse. C.P will also keep your shower and other sumps clean and sweet smelling.

The vent on all tanks-water, fuel, waste holding-has two essential functions: it provides a source of air to replace contents as they are drawn out, and provides an escape route for air displaced by incoming water, fuel or waste. On a waste holding tank, the vent is also the source of air needed to keep the environment in the tank aerobic and odor-free (see the chapter *"Holding Tank Odor—Odor Out the Vent"* for an explanation).

Therefore, it's absolutely essential that all tank vents be kept open, because unless air can be pulled in through the vent to replace the waste (or anything else in any container) being pulled out, a vacuum is created in which nothing more can be removed-but in which strong suction can crack the tank (not likely in fresh water and fuel systems, but highly likely if a waste holding tank is connected to a strong pump-out). A pressurized tank can have equally disastrous consequences-anything from a geyser when the deck pump-out cap is removed to a backup in the toilet, to blown out fittings, to a burst tank.

As with most things, prevention is easier than cure, so always follow these "rules" to prevent both of these problems:

1. Check all your vent through-hulls regularly...carefully clean out the water and fuel tank vent thru-hulls if necessary, backflush the holding tank vent line out with a hose every time you wash the boat. If your tank vent thru-hull isn't designed to allow you to do this—and most "vent" thru-hulls aren't because they're actually designed for use on fuel tank vents, and boat builders just use the same thing on all vents—replace it with an open "bulkhead" thru-hull that does. If a screen is the only thing in the way, knock it out. Screens cause more problems than they solve. Spiders and insects won't be a problem if you backflush the vent line regularly.

Thru-hull
Photo
courtesy of
Forespar

2. Never allow a tank-especially a holding tank-to overflow out the vent; a vent is an *air* vent, it's ***not*** an overflow! Therefore only air should ever be allowed to pass through it. Accidents do happen, though, and they can result in a clogged vent. Cease using the toilet immediately if you see waste coming out the vent and get to a pump-out as soon as possible so that waste doesn't have time to dry and harden in the vent hose. Backflush it out *very* thoroughly with clean water to remove any bits of waste in it. To prevent overflows out the vent, install a gauge.

3. Never just turn pump-out operation over to a dockhand and walk away. Stay there and watch to make certain that the tank is being completely pumped out. Terminate pump-out/dumping at sea immediately if waste stops flowing before the tank is empty. Do not try to pump out or dump the tank again until the vent has been cleared. Making sure the tank vent never becomes blocked is even more important if your boat is serviced by a pump-out service when no one is aboard to pay attention, because pump-out services never bother to make sure the tank empties completely, they just assume it has and disconnect, leaving you with a tank that's still full...and sometimes worse.

4. If you suspect a blocked vent, immediately cease all use of the toilet until you can clear the vent and pump out or legally dump the tank. If you have a manual toilet, stop flushing and cease using the toilet when you feel any backpressure or see any waste backing up into the toilet. If you have an electric toilet, stop flushing the toilet and cease any further use of it if your toilet begins to "burp" or "spit up" flushes, or you begin to experience sluggish discharge

or see that waste has backed up into the bowl, experience sluggish discharge or see that waste has seeped back into the bowl. Waste backing up is not coming from the holding tank, back pressure is preventing the flush from getting to the tank.

CLEARING A BLOCKED VENT

99% of all vent blockages occur at the through-hull. Dirt daubers build nests in the opening, insects fly or crawl in, get stuck and die, dust, dirt and pollen clog screens in the thru-hull. But the through-hull isn't the only place where blockages can occur. Water, fuel or waste can get trapped in any sags in a vent line; eliminate any sags. If rain water or sea water intrusion is an issue, turn the sag into an arch in water or fuel tank vent lines, put a clamshell cover over a holding tank vent. On sailboats, however, heeling can send tank contents into the vent line, also creating a blockage at the tank in both that end of the vent line and the vent fitting on the tank. Overfilling the tank can also cause this on any boat. This will require removing the vent line from the tank (and by the way, it would be a very good idea to open the deck pump-out fitting cap to relieve any pressure before disconnecting any hoses!)

Since most blockages do occur in the through-hull, that's the first place to look. Blast with water; if that doesn't remove the blockage, use the tip of a screwdriver or ice pick to scrape it out. Knock out any screen; as I said before, screens cause more problems than they prevent or solve.

If there's no blockage in the through-hull, check the vent hose for a kink or sag in which water or waste has pooled. Remove the vent hose and clear any clog by blasting water through it (or, it may be easier to replace it). Shorten it to remove any sag.

See...I told you prevention is easier than cure!

Holding tanks should be at least nominally rinsed out after every pump-out or dumpout...thoroughly flushed out 2-4x year depending upon length of your season, and especially in preparation for winter or any other extended layup. It's not hard to do, and all you need is water.

Pump out the tank, or dump it at sea. Then put enough water into the tank via the deck pumpout-because that sends the water into the tank at the bottom to stir up any sludge and hold it in suspension so it can be pumped out-to cover the bottom to a depth of 4-6"...it can be fresh water at the dock or sea water using a wash down pump. Pump out or dump... repeat...repeat...repeat...till you're pumping or dumping clean water.

Human body waste contains animals fats which can build up on tank walls and clog tank gauge senders. So every year or two-or any time you're preparing the boat for winter or other extended layup-it's a good idea to clean out the tank. Follow the above instructions, then fill the tank with clean water and put a gallon (2 gallons if the tank is 50 gallons or larger) of liquid Tide, Wisk or any heavy duty liquid detergent and about 10 lbs. of ice cubes into the tank via the deck pump-out fitting (*not* down the toilet!). Use "homemade" ice, not bagged ice..."homemade" cubes are larger and harder, so they last a lot longer. Go sailing and tack a lot, or go out on a day when seas are bit rough if you're a power boat. Then, if you can, let it sit overnight. Pump out and also run some of the detergent solution through any macerator pump and related plumbing. Fill tank again with clean fresh water...pump out or dump and rinse out again.

Oh stop whining! It's only 2-3 times a year. That much effort won't kill you, and it will prevent problems in the tank!

SANITATION HOSE MAINTENANCE

To prevent sea water mineral buildup in the hoses, flush a cupful-no more than two cupfuls-of undiluted distilled white vinegar ALL the way through the system. Do *not* leave vinegar sitting in the bowl unless you also want to replace the joker valve! Follow the vinegar with clean fresh water after 1 hour. If a buildup has already occurred, flush a 12%-20% solution of muriatic (hydrochloric) acid-available from most hardware stores-through the system. Rinse after one hour, repeat if necessary. Be sure to follow all directions for handling the acid *very* carefully!

THE *NEW* GET RID OF BOAT ODORS

part IV

GETTING RID OF BOAT ODORS

If you're shopping for a boat, and have found one on which everything else passes muster, don't let odor be a deal breaker...it's the easiest and least expensive thing to correct. If the culprit is permeated sanitation hoses, you can insist that the seller replace them as a condition of sale. You'll probably have some residual odor to get rid of, but that's easy. How old is the toilet? What's the make/model? Ask the seller when-if ever-it was rebuilt, or even just had a new joker valve. Depending on the make/model/age of the toilet, you may have another bargaining chip. Just make sure there's nothing ELSE wrong that's a whole lot more serious...so be sure to make any offer "subject to survey" and hire the toughest surveyor you can find.

Unless a tank is leaking, it is rarely if ever the source of odor *inside* the boat because odor from inside the tank has only one place to go: out the tank vent! Odor out the tank vent, which does originate in the tank, is what we're dealing with in this chapter.

Odor out the tank vent line and odor inside the boat are two separate issues. While it's entirely possible to have both, it's equally possible to have one without the other, and each must be dealt with separately. Odor out the tank vent line originates in the tank, not in the plumbing. What very few people in the marine industry have learned, and why there is so much folklore about odor is the very nature of sewage—of *all* organic matter-and how it breaks down, what creates odor, and what prevents odor from forming. Once we understood these principles and learned how to apply them to onboard systems, we were able to install and maintain systems that are completely odor-free and correct the ones that weren't. Once you understand it—and it's so simple!-you can do the same thing.

There are two ways to deal with holding tank odor: try to reduce it, mask it, and contain it after it's formed, by using chemicals and filters—none of which have ever proven very successful...or prevent odor from forming in the first place.

Sewage—all organic material-contains both aerobic (needs oxygen) and anaerobic bacteria (functions in the absence of oxygen); but only the *anaerobic bacteria produce foul-smelling gasses!* Both aerobic and anaerobic bacteria break down organic matter, but when organic matter breaks down aerobically, it converts to CO_2, which is an odorless gas, and water. So, as long as there is a sufficient supply of oxygen to the tank, and an aerobic treatment is added to aid that which naturally occurs in sewage, the aerobic bacteria thrive and overpower the anaerobic bacteria, and the system cannot produce odor.

AEROBIC HOLDING TANK PRODUCTS

A bio-active (live aerobic bacteria) holding tank treatment such as **Raritan "K.O."** works with the aerobic bacteria in sewage, eliminating odor, completely emulsifying solids & paper, and preventing sludge from forming. And because bacteria multiply as long as they have a food source, it's seldom necessary to add between pumpouts. Enzymes alone quickly exhaust themselves because they are not self-renewing, so they can do very little—only a brief respite from odor immediately after adding them-then odor begins to build again. However, they're still a better choice than toxic chemical products. Bio-active (enzyme and bacteria) products are typically more expensive than chemical products because culturing bacteria and enzyme colonies is more expensive than bottling toxic chemicals. Plus, the number of colonies per volume makes a difference in the price. Less expensive bio-active tank products are lower priced because they skimp on the number of bacteria or enzyme colonies. Bioactive products are safe for the environment and for people.

Odorlos is another excellent product. Although not a bio-active product, it too works with nature to prevent odor from occurring in the first place. The active ingredient in Odorlos is nitrates, which extract oxygen from organic matter, preventing the tank contents from becoming anaerobic, and therefore preventing odor. It too is safe for the environment and people.

In fact, aeration alone, if it's properly designed, installed and operated (more about that at the end of this chapter) can eliminate odor with little if any help from a holding tank product and is also people and enviro safe.

CHEMICAL HOLDING TANK PRODUCTS

Chemical products typically only mask one unpleasant odor with another equally unpleasant odor, and in doing so they kill not only odor-causing anaerobic bacteria, but beneficial aerobic bacteria as well—which is not good, because bacteria are needed in the system to break down and emulsify solids and paper. Otherwise, they only break up and dissolve into little tiny particles that settle to the bottom of the tank, along with chemical residue, to become sludge that turns to concrete. Plus, chemicals, unlike bio-active products, are also unwelcome in landside sewage treatment facilities, and are especially unappreciated by those living and working near them!

PREVENTING HOLDING TANK ODOR

Anaerobic bacteria produce a variety of sulfurous gasses—sulfur monoxides and dioxides and hydrogen sulfide (which are the malodorous gasses), methane—which is odorless, but is flammable—and carbon dioxide, which also has no odor but can create an anaerobic environment if there is insufficient ventilation to dissipate it. Carbon dioxide does not rise or fall; it is ambient—like the atmosphere, but heavier than air. Without a sufficient flow of fresh air through the tank to allow it to dissipate, it simply lies like a blanket on top of any pool of sewage (whether inside hose or a holding tank) and builds, creating the perfect environment for the anaerobic bacteria to take over. The system literally "turns septic" and the result: foul gasses out the vent line every time the toilet is flushed or the boat rocks.

So the key to odor control in most tanks is the vent line; it must allow a free exchange of fresh air with the carbon dioxide generated by the sewage. Boat builders, boat owners and boat yard personnel who install holding tanks have always viewed the vent line only as a source of enough air to allow the tank to be pumped out without collapsing and as an exhaust for methane (many even mistakenly believe that methane—which in fact is odorless—to be the source of odor.). Some take the attitude that tanks must inevitably stink, so the thing to do is run that vent line as far from people areas—cockpits, sun decks, etc.—as possible, or make the line as small as possible, or install a filter in it. All of the above actually create the very problem you want to solve.

Think of the holding tank as a stuffy room which needs to be aired. You know that even if there isn't a hint of a breeze outside, just opening a window will allow the fresh air outside to exchange with stuffy air in the room. Open another window for cross-ventilation, and the air exchanges even faster. However, just opening a skylight accomplishes nothing unless there's also a mechanical means (an "attic" or "whole house" fan) of pulling the air up and out—and that won't work unless another window is open to create airflow. But the only "window" into a holding tank is at the end of a "hallway"—the vent line. If that "hallway" is too narrow and goes around corners, takes a long and curved path, or rises more than 45 degrees above horizontal, no ambient air can find its way to the tank to dissipate and exchange itself with the gasses in it.

So the tank vent line should be as short, as straight, and as horizontal as possible, with no sags, no arches, and no bends. The minimum I.D of the hose (which is the "standard" size in use today, but for no reason other than being "standard" in fresh water and fuel tanks) is 5/8". However, I recommend that it be at least 1" or even larger if the boat is large enough to let a larger vent thru-hull be cosmetically acceptable. Ideally, it should be no more than 3' long, but no longer than 5'. If it has to be much longer, or if running the vent line uphill at an angle sharper than 45 degrees can't be avoided, or if it's impossible to run a vent line that does not go around a corner, it may be necessary to install a second vent line in order to create cross ventilation, or install some mechanical means of forcing air through the tank.

My favorite location for a waste tank is the bow—under the v-berth—because the hull just behind the stem (point of the bow) is the only place on the hull except the transom (which is not a good location for a single vent line) that will never be under water even on a sailboat when the boat is at maximum heel. It's the perfect place to install vent-line through-hulls, because the though-hull is always into the wind, forcing air into the vent line, when the boat is underway or on an anchor or mooring. This tank location also requires that the head also be forward in the boat, which often isn't the case so we have no choice but to find another location in the boat that's no further than about 6' from the toilet and also close enough to the hull and high enough in the boat to allow the vent line to be short, straight and relatively horizontal. Burying a waste tank deep in the bilge should be avoided. So should connecting two toilets to a single tank that's more than about 6' from either of them. If one toilet is further away from the tank, two tanks are the only solution!

The vent through-hull should not be a "vent" thru-hull, which are all designed for use on fuel tank vent lines, but boat builders use them on all tank vents because it costs them less to buy the same thing in bulk. Unfortunately they're unsuitable for waste tanks because they permit almost no air flow through the vent. A waste tank vent thru-hull should be a straight open bulkhead type through-hull—one that you can stick a hose nozzle against and back flush the vent line to keep the vent clear.

On sailboats especially it's advisable to vent off the top of the tank and toward the centerline to prevent spills out the vent when the boat is heeled. When the vent is next to the hull, heeling can cause the contents of a half-full or more tank to run into the vent line, and that can lead to a blocked vent.

Check the vent line regularly for blockages; little insects, especially mud daubers, love to build nests in them. So to keep the vent clear, backflush the vent line every time you wash the boat and/or pump out the tank. And remember—the vent line is not an "overflow!" So try never to overfill the tank—and if you do, immediately backflush the vent line thoroughly with water to remove any bits of sewage that can clog it. It's possible for enough air to pass through it to allow the tank to be pumped and gasses to escape, but that doesn't mean the line is completely clear of any blockage.

Finally, the system, including the tank, should be at least nominally rinsed, through the deck fill—with fresh or salt water—after each pump-out, and occasionally with fresh water. If your marina doesn't have a dock water hose for this purpose, please ask them to install one. It should be separate from the potable water hose, and the two hoses should never be interchanged. *See the chapter "Maintaining the Holding Tank" for more details.*

VENT LINE FILTERS

I wish I could have invented a product that actually helps to create the very problem it's sold to solve, because that's what a vent line filter does. Filters do trap the gasses which try to escape through the vent line, but they impede the free exchange of air needed to prevent odor from forming in the first place, eliminating the need for a filter! What's more, they only last about a year, are toast immediately if they get wet-which makes it impossible to backflush the vent line to prevent blockages-and are ridiculously expensive. So install a vent line filter only as a last resort, because gasses that can't easily pass through the vent line will go wherever they can-into hoses, eventually permeating even the best ones.

AERATION AS A SOLUTION TO HOLDING TANK ODOR

As of this writing, the Groco Sweetank System is the only holding tank aeration system on the market. That's been the case since Groco first introduced it in 2002, which is a good indication that there's considerably more engineering to a tank aeration system than most people think. If there weren't, the Sweetank would surely have plenty of competition by now.

Aerating the tank contents can be an excellent solution on many boats. However, it may not be as simple a solution as it sounds for all boats. For one thing, the aerator pump must be big enough for the size of the tank. If it's too small, it only forces foul air out the vent instead of oxygenating the waste. And the piping inside can't only provide just a single column of air; it must be laid across the bottom of the tank to create a "curtain" of air throughout the tank contents.

For another, the pump must run 24/7/365 (except, of course, during winter or other extended layup) or the tank will turn anaerobic, which means the boat must always have a source of power to keep it running. That can make aeration a problematic solution on trailered boats, boats that are dry stored in "racks," or on moorings, or in slips without shore power, because when the pump doesn't run for days, especially in warm weather, the tank becomes anaerobic. A tank that has turned anaerobic can be recovered but it takes several hours, even a day or longer, during which time the gasses forced out the vent by the aerator can be quite horrific for a while until they gradually start to diminish.

So while aeration is one solution-and a very good one-to holding tank odor out the vent on many boats, it's not a "one size fits all" answer for every boat. But then, very few things are.

PERMEATED SANITATION HOSES

Permeated sanitation hoses are the most common source of odor inside the boat, and there's no predicting how long it will take for a hose to permeate; brand new hose permeated on one of my own boats in less than 3 months-the very same brand and type of hose had been on my previous boat for nearly 7 years without a trace of odor. What causes hose to permeate? Sewage and/or sea water left to stand in it. Sanitation hose absorbs water. The better quality the hose, the slower the rate at which it absorbs it, but all rubber and flexible PVC hose absorbs water at some rate. If that water stinks, it will cause the hose to stink once it's soaked up enough of it, and once a hose has become permeated (saturated) with odor, it cannot be reversed...the only cure is replacement. But it can be prevented, or at least delayed. How?

Ideally the tank should be no more than 6 feet from the toilet, because that's as far as waste will travel in the average amount of time that most people will pump a manual toilet or leave their finger on a flush button. The absolute maximum distance is 10 feet. Any further from the toilet and waste will be left to sit in the hose to permeate it unless the system is plumbed to provide help from gravity.

The discharge hose, no matter whether it goes overboard, to a Type I or II MSD, or to a holding tank, should be installed, if at all possible, with no sags or low places where sewage can stand. When a marine toilet is not flushed sufficiently to clear the hose of sewage and rinse the hose behind the sewage, that sewage sits in low spots in the hose or bits of it cling to the walls of the hose—getting no air, allowing the anaerobic bacteria to thrive and produce their stinking gasses. If sewage stands in a low spot which gets no air in a hose that's susceptible to a high rate of water absorption, it will permeate the hose very quickly. This is what has given rise to the myth that the "wrong" hose causes odor. Therefore, it's important to flush your toilet thoroughly enough to clear the entire hose of sewage and rinse behind it. However, 9 people out of 10 stop flushing as soon as the bowl is empty—they don't even move it the 6 feet mentioned earlier!- instead of flushing till the bowl contents have been washed all the way through the system. So each flush sits in the discharge line, pushed another foot or two by the next flush and the next... sitting in the hose all the while, producing stinky gasses that are soaked up by the hose.

"But I don't want to fill up my tank with flush water!!" you cry, and I don't blame you. So if longer flushes every time is just asking too much, at least run a quart or two of clean fresh water (use a cup from the sink if your toilet uses sea water) down the toilet once a day, last thing before you go to bed. Another solution is a loop immediately after the toilet that's higher than the top of the holding tank. Very few people know that any manual toilet that's working anywhere near factory specs can move bowl contents up to 4 vertical feet or 6 linear feet in the dry mode. So pump long enough in the wet mode to move bowl contents over the loop, follow that with a couple of pumps to supply rinse water, then switch to the dry mode to push the rinse water over the top of the loop. Gravity will get your flush and your rinse water the rest of the way to the tank.

How do you know if permeated hoses are the source of your odor? The odor is unique—it may be a sharp, sour, only somewhat sewer-like odor that's a result of the chemical interaction between the waste and the hose material. If your boat smells like a swamp or has very definite sewer odor, you may or may not have permeated sanitation hoses, but there may also be another source: hoses are the most common source of odor inside a boat, not the only source..

Because odors are always strongest at their source, if hoses are the culprit, the odor will be strongest in the lockers and other areas the hoses pass through, under, or behind.

If you're still in any doubt after poking your nose into all the places the hoses go, there's a simple test that's never wrong: clean off the outside of a section of hose where the odor is the strongest (this is to remove any odors from another source that may have attached themselves to the outside of the hose). Wet a clean rag in hot water, wring it out and wrap it around the hose. Use a clean rag for every section of hose. When the rag has cooled, remove it and smell it. If you can't smell anything on the rag, that hose is not the source of your odor problem. But if you can smell the same odor on the rag, that hose has become permeated, and once a hose has become permeated with odor, it cannot be reversed; replacing the hose is the only cure. Since that's a job that's no fun at all, prevention is well worth the time and effort it takes.

"HEAD" ODORS

Toilets that use "raw" water, especially sea water, typically have more odor problems than toilets that use fresh water supplied by the onboard fresh water system, or from a lake or river. Sea water, especially coastal sea water and some lake and river water too, is alive with animal and vegetable micro (and not-so-micro) organisms, When that water is left to sit and stagnate in the toilet intake line and pump, or worse yet, a not-so-micro-critter becomes trapped in the intake line, pump and/or the channel in the rim of the bowl, they die, decay and stink—and they stink a lot worse in hot weather than in cool weather (everything does). If you aren't sure whether that's at one of the sources of your odor problem, there are a couple of indicators:

The odor is concentrated in the head and not pervasive throughout the cabin-or at least is much worse in the head than in the rest of the boat.

The odor is much worse after the boat has been sitting for a few days than while you're aboard and flushing the toilet regularly—in fact, it either goes away or is greatly reduced after you've flushed the toilet a few times when you first come aboard again.

You may see dark flecks from the channel in the rim of the bowl if the source is the remains of trapped animal or vegetable sea life.

To find out if this is your problem, close the seacock and flush the toilet as dry as possible. Disconnect the hose from the through-hull and stick that end of it in a bucket of water to which you've added a quart of distilled white vinegar. Pump/flush the whole bucketful through the system. Do not reconnect the hose to the through-hull yet, flush only with clean fresh water while you're aboard this time. How to do that depends on whether your toilet is manual or electric:

If you have a manual toilet, use cups of fresh water from the sink to flush the toilet for the entire weekend.

If your toilet is an electric model with a single button that simultaneously pulls in flush water and discharges bowl contents, flushing it dry (without bringing in flush water) may "fry" the intake impeller, so it will be necessary to leave the hose in a bucket, making sure there's always water in it. (Stop complaining, it's just for one weekend!)

If the odor is gone when you come back to the boat next weekend, bingo! you've found the source of your odor problem. If you still have odor, and it's still confined to the head compartment, clean your shower sump.

The best way to prevent seawater intake odors depends upon what kind of toilet you have and several other factors. But no matter what type of toilet you have, nothing poured into the bowl can help because anything poured into the bowl just goes out the discharge...it doesn't recirculate (and be glad it doesn't!) through the channel in the rim of the bowl or the pump or the intake line, which is where the odor is coming from. Nor do I recommend keeping the intake thru-hull closed and always using a cup from the sink or the shower head to supply flush water for the same reason: no water going through the top half of the pump creates friction that wears out rubber parts in it.

I don't recommend using the "inline" chemical devices sold for this purpose. Some only reduce the problem, they don't completely solve it. The chemicals used in some of them can be harmful to rubber and neoprene parts in the toilet; others may be incompatible with holding tank products, and may even produce toxic gasses when combined with some of them. And an inline device should never be used if a Type I or Type II treatment device is installed, because the chemicals in them can damage the device—especially the electrodes in a ElectroScan or Electro Scan—and interfere with treatment in other devices.

Most electric macerating toilets are now available in both raw water and pressurized fresh water versions, so replacing the toilet is one solution. But it's also an expensive solution that may not be an option for boat owners who already have "raw water" flush electric toilets installed and aren't shopping for a new toilet. Furthermore, replacing a manual toilet with an electric one may not be a viable option on smaller sailboats or power cruisers that have limited 12v power resources. And connecting *any* raw water flush toilet to the onboard fresh water system is definitely *not* an option! That cannot be done without risk of polluting the fresh water or damaging the toilet, or both, and every toilet manufacturer specifically warns against doing so in their installation instructions. *Only* toilets that are designed by the manufacturer to use pressurized water should ever be connected to the fresh water system. However, there is a very simple, inexpensive and safe solution for the owners of most manual and electric raw water toilets.

SIMPLE CURE FOR SEA WATER INTAKE ODOR

HOW TO INSTALL:

Sink drain thru-hulls are below the waterline on almost all sailboats. Some sailboat builders even plumb the head sink drain and the toilet intake to share the same thru-hull because it accomplishes two things: it eliminates one below-waterline hole in the boat and it saves the boat builder the cost of one thru-hull and seacock. Although most powerboat sink drain thru-hulls are above the waterline, the toilet intake thru-hulls are below waterline on all boats, and there's certainly no reason why the sink and toilet intake on any sailboat or powerboat can't share the same **below**-waterline thru-hull regardless of which one it is, provided the toilet and sink are on the same side of the keel and the thru-hull is close to both.

If the head sink drains below waterline, it's a simple matter to re-route the toilet intake hose to tee or wye it into the sink drain line as close to the seacock as possible because the connection must be below waterline to work. Or, if the head sink drains *above* waterline, do it in reverse—reroute the sink drain line to connect anywhere in the toilet intake line. Both hoses are typically the same size— ¾" ID—on most boats. If they're not, no problem...just make sure to buy a tee fitting that fits both sizes.

HOW TO USE:

After you've closed the toilet intake seacock in preparation to close up the boat (you do close all seacocks before leaving the boat to sit??), fill the sink with clean fresh water and flush the toilet. Because the seacock is closed, the toilet will draw the water out of the sink, rinsing the sea water out of the entire system—intake line, pump, channel in the rim of the bowl and the discharge line. If your toilet is electric, be careful not to let it run dry...doing so can burn out the intake impeller.

It may also be necessary to keep the sink plugged except when in use, with a rubber sink plug or by installing a conveniently located shut-off valve in the drain hose. Otherwise the toilet may pull air through the sink when you try to flush, preventing the pump from priming.

Or Your Holding Tank!

"We're at our wits' end...we never use the tank for "#2." We never leave anything sitting in the tank, we ALWAYS pump out and rinse out the tank at the end of every weekend/cruise. We've tried every holding tank product, and we've installed a larger vent line, but we cannot get rid of the odor in our boat! Help!!"

If that sounds familiar, it's because your holding tank isn't the source of your odor! In fact, the tank is rarely if ever the source of odor *inside* the boat. Why? Because unless the tank is leaking, odor from inside the tank has only one place to go: out the tank vent! So while frequent pumpouts, increased ventilation, various tank products may or may not have any impact at all on odor out the tank vent, using any or all of them to try to eliminate odor inside the boat is only chasing your tail ...you'll never catch it. So let's talk about the real sources of odor inside a boat and how to eliminate them, starting with...

BILGES

You cannot eliminate any odor unless you first remove *all* the source(s) of that odor!

I get calls all the time from people who've torn out most of their sanitation system trying to get rid of what they thought was "head odor," when all they really needed to do was clean their bilges-really *clean* them for a change, and rinse all the dirty water out, instead of just dumping more "miracle" cleaning product into the swamp and calling it done.

A wet bilge is a dark stagnant swamp.... And it behaves like one, growing a variety of molds, fungi and bacteria—some that thrive in dark stagnant water, others that just like damp dark places...and it generates the same gasses-hydrogen sulfide and sulfur dioxide-that can make a whole boat smell like rotten eggs or a sewer. The warmer the weather and water, the faster they grow. Add some dead and decaying sea water micro-organisms, dirt, food particles, rain water, wash water, hot weather and humidity, plus a little oil or diesel, and you have a real primordial soup...no wonder it stinks!

Most people's approach to bilge cleaning consists only of throwing some bilge cleaner/ and or bleach into that soup when it starts to stink and calling it done. I've never understood why they think that's all there is to it. They wouldn't just add some detergent and bleach to a bathtub full of dirty bath water, swish it around a bit, then just pull the plug and expect the bathtub to be clean. Or just pour some more dishwashing detergent into a sinkful of dirty greasy dishwater, swish it around a bit, then pull the plug and expect to have a clean sink. So why do so many boat owners think they can have a clean bilge without any effort and especially without rinsing *all* the dirty water out of it? So if you really want to get rid of odor inside your boat, roll up your sleeves and get to work!

1. As noted above (and in several other places in this book), you can't get rid of any odor unless you first eliminate the source of that odor. So before starting any cleaning you need to find and fix any oil leaks, replace any permeated hoses and remove any other sources of odor.

2. Bilge pads and "pillows" no longer can separate oil from water and collect the oil once detergent or degreasers are mixed with oil. So before using any degreaser, detergent or other cleaning product, put them down to sop up all the oil and/or diesel possible. Replace pads/pillows as necessary and dispose of them in approved sites.

3. Scrub the bilges. In my experience, a power washer is the best way to clean a bilge, because it gets into places you can't reach.

4. The most important step: Flush all the dirty water out! A wet dirty bilge **is** a primordial soup! You won't get it clean by just dumping something into it, then letting the bilge pump dispose of the dirty water, even if you have scrubbed it...any more than you'd end up with a clean kitchen sink if did nothing more than pour some Dawn into greasy dirty dishwater, scrubbed the sink, and then just pulled the plug.

5. Use a shop vac, or dinghy bailer, bucket and sponge to mop up the remaining water, then leave hatches open so it can completely dry out for 12-24 hours. Turning fans on if possible helps to accomplish that.

Now you finally have a clean bilge and are ready to eliminate the residual odor.

There is a product that I tripped over at a boat show in Seattle several years ago and brought samples home to test. It's called PureAyre and is available from pet supply stores and Amazon too, as well as directly from the company http://www/pureayre.com and is the only product I've found that will not only eliminate "organic" (sewage, mold etc.) odors, but also diesel, oil and even smoke odors. This stuff works! Put a gallon undiluted in a pump garden spray jug (unless you enjoy wearing out your hand on a trigger sprayer) and just lightly "hose down" every surface, nook and cranny in your bilges, inside bait/fish boxes, lockers, and any place else that's smelly-including the inside of your boat shoes!-even the inside of the fridge; it's approved for use around food. It also does a great job on cushions, musty foulies and PFDs. But remember: PureAyre is not a cleaning product! Use it only to remove residual odors after you've thoroughly cleaned and removed all the sources of odors.

DO NOT RINSE!!! Just leave lockers—including the fridge or ice box, and all hatches etc. open for 24 hours. Run fans if possible, and put soft goods and anything else that isn't bolted down out in the sun all day.

A FEW WORDS ABOUT BILGE CLEANERS

Whether a bilge cleaner is environmentally friendly, or even "biodegradable" (a meaningless feel-good term intended to mislead you in believing it means the same thing as "environmentally friendly"...it doesn't!) is immaterial because no cleaning product can magically turn the grease, oil and diesel in a bilge into an environmentally friendly mixture. Detergents and degreasers only emulsify petroleum products so that they sink instead of putting an oily sheen on the water when your bilge pumps dump it overboard. And it's never ceased to amaze me that the same people who have spasms at the idea of pumping a little truly biodegradable toilet waste overboard think nothing of just dumping a "biodegradable" bilge cleaner into a bilge full of oily water and letting the bilge pumps send it overboard.

SUMPS

Sumps are another overlooked source of boat odor. Somehow it never occurs to most people that shower sumps and drain are full of bacteria, hair, soap scum and body oils that become another "primordial soup." And the shower sump may not be the only sump. Central heat/air conditioning condensate and sailboat ice boxes often drain into sumps instead of into the bilge. Left alone long enough, a wet dirty sump can smell like a sewer even faster than a wet dirty bilge. It's another wet dark place, ideal for growing odor-producing "critters."

Keeping drains, sumps, and sump pumps—and strainers too-clean is actually one of the easiest jobs on a boat, one of the few that doesn't require any manual labor: Just put a few ounces of Raritan "C.P. Cleans Potties" into them once a week when it can stand at least overnight. "C.P. Cleans Potties" is an amazing product, part of the product line my own company developed and sold to Raritan in 1999. Although the name implies that it's only a toilet bowl cleaner, it's a bio-enzymatic cleaner that not only kills odor on contact, but the enzymes in it also "eat" hair, soap scum, grease, and oils. It does need time to work, though, which is why you need to use it when it can stand at least overnight.

To clean sumps: Make sure the sump is about 1/4-1/3 full of water...put 2-3 ounces of C.P. down the shower drain. That's it. When you come back, run plenty of clean water through the sump to rinse it out.

Sink drains: close the seacocks...put an ounce or two of C.P. down the drain...fill the drain with water. That's it. When you come back, open the seacock and flush out the drain with clean water.

Although C.P. ceases to accomplish anything after about 24 hours, it can sit in drains and sumps indefinitely without any problem, so no rush to get back and flush it out. Use it once a week, or just before the boat will sit each time and your drains and sumps will stay clean and sweet smelling and screens and sump pumps will remain clog free. And oh, by the way, C.P. is also an outstanding toilet bowl cleaner that's compatible with any tank treatment and safe to use in any Type I or II MSD.

CHAIN/ANCHOR LOCKER

The most overlooked source of odor on a boat is the chain locker, especially in salt water. Those same critters that can make a sea water toilet intake stink are all over your wet anchor rode, fermenting in your chain locker in the summer heat. Once or twice a year, take the entire rode out, lay it on the dock and rinse it thoroughly with clean fresh water, then let it dry. And while the rode is drying on the dock, take advantage of the opportunity to clean the locker the same way you'll clean the bilge-with a good detergent and a thorough rinse, and-if possible-a good airing out...open the cabin access and aim a fan at it.

TRAPPED WATER

Occasionally I hear from people who've done all of the above, but still can't get rid of a swampy sewer-like odor, especially after their boat has been closed up for a while. If that's the case, water has to be trapped below decks somewhere. A limber hole may be blocked—or never put in-keeping water from running out of an area. Water may be finding its way in from the deck. Or, it may be just bad boat design. But until you find the water and remove it, it'll continue to stink—and can also lead to hidden rot. So it's essential that you find and remove any trapped water.

Doing that may require installing new hatches in the cabin sole. The mere thought of doing that makes some boat owners cringe. But there's nothing sacrosanct about the way the boat left the factory; production boat building is based more on cost than on doing things the best way. So feel free to make whatever modifications are necessary to create the necessary access that allows you to properly maintain your boat—to get to equipment and keep everything clean and dry. You'll only be improving your boat, and you'll be very glad you did!

MOLD AND MILDEW

Fresh air and sunlight are the most effective enemies of molds and mildew, but there isn't much of either one in a closed up cabin. So you want to allow the air that is available to circulate in every nook and cranny. When closing up the boat, leave lockers and drawers slightly open to allow air to get into them. Installing solar or 12 volt vent fans that pull air through the boat will help a lot. On the first warm sunny day in the spring, put all your soft goods—cushions, mattresses, rugs etc.—along with life jackets and foul weather gear outside on the deck for the day. While they're out, clean the hard surfaces and wipe with a mild solution of bleach and water or better yet, some PureAyre.

A FEW WORDS ABOUT OZONE GENERATORS

Ozone in any concentration strong enough to do any good is not only a health hazard, it's also *highly* corrosive and destructive to rubber, neoprene and flexible PVC—in other words, every seal, valve and hose on a boat.

According to the EPA, "Available scientific evidence shows that, at concentrations that do not exceed public health standards, ozone is generally ineffective in controlling indoor air pollution. The concentration of ozone would have to greatly exceed health standards to be effective in removing most indoor air contaminants. In the process of reacting with chemicals indoors, ozone can produce other chemicals that can be irritating and corrosive.

As for how well the portable ozone generators work when it comes to getting rid of odors... yes, people who've bought them rave about how well they work. And, yes, the manufacturer's do assure you that the ozone concentration is well below that which can present any health hazard. But if that's true, they can't deliver enough ozone to destroy the sources of any odors. If they did deliver enough ozone to destroy the sources of odors, it should only be necessary to run one occasionally to destroy a new odor source. But among all the people you know who've bought ozone generators, have you ever met anyone who has ever been able to turn it off without having odors return? That should be enough to tell you that ozone generators are only very expensive air fresheners, because they don't deliver enough ozone to be anything else. Save your money and get rid of the sources of your odors! Eliminating the source is the only thing that really works.

part V

TO EVERYTHING THERE IS A SEASON

More boats have to be towed in, or find themselves back in the yard, and more equipment failures happen in the spring than at any other time of year. And the owners all say the same thing: "I don't know what's wrong...it was working fine when we put the boat away last fall." Here's how to make sure you're not one of them!

PRE-LAUNCH:

Check all your through-hulls and seacocks for signs of corrosion or other failure, lubricate and re-bed as necessary. Check all below-waterline hose connections and replace any cracked or broken fittings or corroded hose clamps. (And don't limit this exercise to your sanitation system!)

Bedding compound is a lot cheaper than replacing a water-stained headliner or repairing rotted fiberglass! So check all your deck hardware—rail stanchions, cleats, winches, etc.—for signs that bedding is failing, and rebed as necessary.

If you haven't done it in at least two years, change every impeller—in the electric toilet, the macerator, the engine intakes-on the boat, even if it looks fine. Each time an impeller pump starts up, it runs dry at least briefly which wears down the edges of the vanes. Unless it's run dry long enough to really fry it, you can't see the wear, and there's only about the width of a human hair between an impeller that still fits tightly enough in the housing to pump water and one that doesn't. Impellers also dry out over the winter and become hard and brittle...they're more prone to failure in the spring than any other time. And a hard dry impeller can score the housing, requiring its replacement too.

If you have access to water, now is a great time to really clean your bilges, sumps and chain locker because it provides time for them to dry out of completely. You won't smell them now, but there are a lot of odor-causing "critters" growing in all those places, just waiting to multiply and stink when the weather gets warm.

Manual toilets: If you haven't rebuilt your toilet in at least 5 years, now's the time to do it, while it's clean and dry. Preventive maintenance-new seals, gaskets, valves, etc.—reduces the odds of having to make repairs by 99%. Whether you rebuild or not, if you didn't do it in the fall, lubricate your manual toilet: open the pump (see instructions in the Chapter "*Maintaining Marine Toilets*") and give it a liberal slathering with the same thick Teflon or silicon grease (I recommend Superlube, available from Ace Hardware) that was in it when it left the factory. Not only will it keep your toilet pumping smoothly for a full season, but it will protect the seals and pump housing from grit and dirt. Use the same grease to lubricate "Y-valves," seacocks, winches—anything that spends a lot of time being wet.

Check all vent lines-on fuel, water and holding tanks-for obstructions (dirt daubers love to build nests in thru-hulls) and clean them out if necessary. Pressure test your holding tank for leaks. Check hoses for odor permeation and replace if necessary-it's a much more pleasant job in cool weather and when the system is clean and dry-than in hot when they're full of sewage. Clean or replace air valves in vented loops.

POST LAUNCH:

Test your toilet to make sure it's working correctly. Especially in electric toilets, things have a way of drying over the winter. The time to find out is before you stock the fridge and take your boss or in-laws out for the first spring cruise! Flush all the antifreeze out of the system with fresh water...but don't add any treatment to the tank until you're ready to use it. Flush that down the toilet with the first "real" flush.

DON'T FORGET THE FRESH WATER SYSTEM!

Although most people think only in terms of the tank, the plumbing is actually the source of most foul water, because the molds, mildew, fungi and bacteria which cause it thrive in damp dark places, not under water. There are all kinds of products sold that claim to keep onboard water fresh, but all that's really necessary is an annual or in especially warm climates, semi-annual recommissioning of the entire system—tank and plumbing. The following recommendations conform to section 10.8 in the A-1 192 code covering electrical, plumbing, and heating of recreational vehicles. The solution is approved and recommended by competent health officials. It may be used in a new system, a used one that has not been used for a period of time, or one that may have been contaminated.

Before beginning, turn off hot water heater at the breaker; do not turn it on again until the entire recommissioning is complete. Icemakers should be left running to allow cleaning out of the water feed line; however the first two buckets of ice—the bucket generated during recommissioning and the first bucketful afterward-should be discarded... bleach does absolutely nothing to improve the flavor of good Scotch!

1. Prepare a chlorine solution using one gallon of water and 1/4 cup (2 oz. or 25 ml) Clorox or Purex household bleach (5% sodium Hypochlorite solution). With tank empty, pour chlorine solution into tank. Use one gallon of solution for each 5 gallons of tank capacity. (Those are the "official" directions. They work out to 1 quart or litre of bleach/50 gallons of water tank capacity, which is *much* easier to calculate!)

2. Complete filling of tank with fresh water. Open each faucet and drain cock until air has been released and the entire system is filled. Do not turn off the pump; it must remain on to keep the system pressurized and the solution in the lines

3. Allow to stand for at least three hours, but no longer than 24 hours.

4 Drain through every faucet on the boat (and if you haven't done this in a while, it's a good idea to remove any diffusion screens from the faucets, because what's likely to come out will clog them). Fill the tank again with fresh water only, drain again through every faucet on the boat.

5. To remove excess chlorine taste or odor which might remain, prepare a solution of one quart white vinegar to five gallons water and allow this solution to agitate in tank for several days by vessel motion.

6. Drain tank again through every faucet, and flush the lines again by filling the tank 1/4-1/2 full and again flushing with potable water.

People have expressed concern about using this method to recommission aluminum tanks. While bleach (chlorine) is corrosive, its effects are cumulative. So the effect of an annual or semi-annual "shock treatment" is negligible compared to the cumulative effect of holding chlorinated city water in the tank for years. And it's that cumulative effect that makes it a *very* bad idea to add a little bleach to each fill. Not only does it damage the system, but unless you add enough to make your water taste and smell like laundry, it's not enough to do any good. Even if it were, any "purifying" properties in chlorine evaporate within 24 hours, leaving behind only the corrosive properties. Nevertheless, it's a good idea to mix the total amount of bleach needed for recommissioning in a few gallons of water before putting it into an empty stainless or aluminum tank.

An annual or semi-annual recommissioning according to the above directions is all that should be necessary to keep your water tasting and smelling as good as anything that comes out of any faucet on land. If you need to improve on that, install a water filter. Just remember that a filter is not a substitute for cleaning out the system, and that filters require regular inspection and cleaning or replacement.

To keep the water system cleaner longer, *use* your fresh water...keep water flowing through system. The molds, fungi, and bacteria only start to grow in hoses that aren't being used. Before filling the tank each time, always let the dock water run for at least 15 minutes first...the same critters that like the lines on your boat *love* the dock supply line and your hose that sits in the warm sun, and you certainly don't want to transfer water that's been sitting in the dock supply line to your boat's system. So let the water run long enough to flush out all the water that's been standing in them so that what goes into your boat is coming straight from the water main.

There are two ways to winterize fresh water and sanitation plumbing: with antifreeze and without antifreeze. If you opt for the "no antifreeze" method, all the water must be removed from the entire system. Why? Because it's not freezing temperatures that break pipes and crack tanks, it's because ice occupies about 10% more space than the same amount as water...and when it expands, something has to give—and that something will be your water or holding tank, water heater, hose connection, water pipe, or toilet bowl.

There are boat owners who advocate using cheap vodka to winterize the fresh water system. *Bad* idea! Although undiluted 80 proof booze doesn't freeze in a home freezer, -10 F is the maximum low temp in most freezers and refrigerators, and -10 is considered a midwinter heat wave in some places that border the Great Lakes! Worse yet, although undiluted booze won't freeze, it will freeze solid if it's cut as little as 8 parts vodka/2 parts water. Think about it: if there are two gallons of water left in your water tank, eight gallons of vodka wouldn't be enough to prevent it from freezing! So the next time you hear someone advocate using cheap vodka as alternative to antifreeze, ask them two questions: 1. Do you keep your boat in the water all winter? 2. Does the water freeze over? I'll be bet real money that the answer to the first question will be yes and the and the answer to second question will be no, in which case they don't need to winterize at all! Everything below the waterline on a boat takes its temperature from the hull temperature, and the hull is the same temperature as the water it's sitting in. Which means that if the boat is in the water and the water never freezes, nothing below the waterline on the boat can freeze either. So if you keep your boat in the water somewhere, all you need to do is drain the system and leave the faucets open so that any water in the plumbing can drain, The rest of you need to winterize correctly. If you choose to use antifreeze, recommissioning the system according to the directions included in the *"Spring Recommissioning"* section of Part V to remove all traces of it.

Let's start with the fresh water system:

ANTIFREEZE METHOD (EASIEST)

1. Drain the water tanks completely (just turn on all the faucets).
2. Drain water heater. Most have a drain petcock; follow manufacturer's instructions to find it and use it. Remove both the inlet and outlet hoses, and if necessary use a shop vac to be sure of getting all the water out of it.
3. Do *not* put antifreeze in the water heater. Connect water heater inlet and outlet hoses together to bypass it. Bypass kits for this purpose are available from boat stores and RV supply stores.
   Why drain the water heater and bypass it instead putting antifreeze into it? Because you'd need as many gallons as the water heater tank holds—which would cost a fortune!-and it takes forever to flush that much out of it in the spring!
4. Add non-toxic antifreeze ("the pink stuff") and pump that through the system until all outlets-hot and cold in the galley, head, shower, and any deck wash-only antifreeze. Leave all the faucets open to make sure there is no pressure in the system.

NO ANTIFREEZE "DRY" METHOD:

1. Follow the first *three* steps listed above.

2. Using an air compressor, blow *all* the air out of *all* the plumbing, disconnecting it where necessary to achieve this. The first time you opt for this method can be difficult and labor intensive, but if connections are reassembled in the spring using quick-connect fittings, it becomes a lot easier in the future.

SANITATION SYSTEM

The sanitation system is the easy job:

Pump holding tank out, then rinse thoroughly to flush out any sludge. This does not require filling the tank and can even be done with sea water. Here's how: Put enough water into the tank via the deck pump-out fitting—because that sends the water into the tank at the bottom to stir up any sludge and holds it in suspension so it can be flushed out– to cover the bottom to a depth of a couple of inches. Pump that out. Repeat...repeat... repeat...till you're pumping out clean water. Then add water one more time and turn on the macerator to rinse it out along with the overboard discharge plumbing.

Alternatively, you can use a wash down pump to do the whole job. Stick it in the pump-out out fitting and turn on the water. When the depth reaches a couple of inches, turn on the macerator and let it run till the water runs clean (it may be best to do this offshore outside the "3 mile limit").

Now you're ready to winterize the system.

Sea water toilet, manual or electric: Just flushing antifreeze through the bowl will not protect the intake line, the toilet pump or the bowl...it'll only go out the discharge to the tank. To protect the whole system, it's necessary to close the toilet intake through-hull, disconnect inlet hose and stick it in a gallon of non-toxic ("the pink stuff") antifreeze. Pump the whole gallon through the system into the holding tank. Do not reconnect head intake hose to the through-hull.

If your toilet inlet line is teed into the head sink drain line, you can add the antifreeze by just pouring it down the sink-after you've closed the drain seacock, of course! Pump the head or hold the button down long enough to get the excess fluid out of the system.

Fresh water toilet: If your toilet uses onboard pressurized fresh water, you winterized it when you winterized your fresh water system. All that remains is, flush the appropriate amount of non-toxic antifreeze ("the pink stuff") down the toilet into the tank and you're done.

After the boat comes out of the water, open all the sea cocks to drain any trapped water.

Do not use antifreeze in an ElectroScan, Lectra/San, PuraSan, or any other Type I or Type II MSD. Follow manufacturer's instructions to winterize all Type I and II MSDs. After the boat comes out of the water, open all the sea cocks to drain any trapped water.

And you're done.

part VI

FREQUENTLY ASKED QUESTIONS

THE ONES ASKED MOST FREQUENTLY

Why are marine toilets called "heads?

The term originated because the first toilet facilities on boats were nothing more than holes in the hull in the bow of the boat-which was known as the "head of the ship"-where they could be well below decks and where the bow wake could wash it away from the hull. On smaller ships, if the seas were rough, users often got their bottoms (and a lot more) washed by waves that came up through the holes...which might not have been too bad an experience in the warmer latitudes, but no fun at all in the icy waters of say, the North Atlantic! Like many other terms, the name "head" continued to refer to the toilet compartment even after it became no longer necessary to put it in the head of the ship.

Where did the practice of pouring oil into marine toilets to lubricate them originate?

Manual marine toilets originally had leather seals, valves, o-rings and gaskets. Because leather soaks up oil, a good dose of vegetable oil flushed down the toilet periodically was a very effective lubricant that prevented leathers from drying out and lasted quite a while. But vegetable oil—or anything else that's thin enough to pour down the toilet—is pretty much worthless as a lubricant in today's marine toilets because rubber and neoprene has replaced leather in all toilets except a couple of all bronze "thrones," and rubber and neoprene can't absorb oil. But people insist on pouring oil down the toilet anyway, even though it all washes out in just a few flushes.

What is a macerator?

A macerator is essentially a blender blade in an electric toilet or overboard discharge pump and works pretty much the same way as a blender; it "purees" solids and paper as they pass through the pump. That's all it does. A macerator is not a pump; it's a doodad in a discharge pump or electric toilet. In a macerating electric toilet it's the pump that pushes the macerated ("pureed") waste through the discharge hose. Same is true of a "macerator" that dumps a tank at sea. What's commonly known as "macerator" is just short for "macerator pump." The pump pulls the tank contents out of the tank and pushes it through the macerator blades and sends it overboard.

My overboard discharge macerator pump runs, but doesn't pump anything out of the tank. Why?

If the motor keeps shutting down—blowing its internal "breaker"—there's either a clog in the pump that's preventing the impeller from spinning, or because waste is sticky, if the macerator hasn't been used recently, there's a good chance that the impeller is stuck tight to the inside of its housing and can't spin...either of which will cause the motor to overheat and shut down.

If the motor stays on, the tank vent may be blocked. If you're sure that's not the problem and also sure that the discharge thru-hull and any "Y-valve" are open, the most likely reason is a failed or worn out impeller.

Even a macerator pump that's used regularly should get a new impeller every spring. Even the brief couple of seconds that the pump runs dry before it primes wears a little off the edges of the vanes. When it hasn't been used recently, the impeller tends to stick to the housing, putting stress on the vanes when the pump starts. If the first start-up doesn't break a vane, it cracks one, which breaks completely the *next* time. It's a lot more fun to replace the impeller when the macerator pump isn't full of waste than when it is. The possibility that you might have to is also a very good reason to have a "Y-valve" in the tank discharge line, not just a tee.

Any macerator pump that's sat in the boat unused for more than a couple of seasons is likely to be "toast." Lack of use, especially in a salt air environment, does more damage than constant use because rubber and neoprene dries out and becomes brittle, motor lubrication settles and ceases to offer much if any protection from corrosion. So if it hasn't been used, or won't be used, for more than a season, the best thing to do is remove it. You or the next owner can always replace it if/when there's a need for it.

Why is there always an inch of waste left in my holding tank after pump-out?

When the level in the tank drops below the top of the tank discharge fitting, air gets into the discharge hose, causing the pump-out or overboard discharge pump to lose its prime. Once it's lost prime, it can't pull any more out of the tank. This is actually a good thing, because it prevents sludge from drying out and turning into "concrete."

My toilet is electric. The motor runs, but nothing goes down.

Before you take the toilet apart, eliminate all the other possibilities:

First make sure the tank vent isn't blocked. If the air in the tank displaced by incoming waste can't get out, the tank pressurizes, creating back pressure. Enough back pressure and the toilet can't flush against it. The easiest way to check: Verrrry carefully loosen the deck pump-out cap. Have a firm grip on it, and have the hose handy; if your tank is so pressurized that it's preventing the toilet from flushing, you'll have an eruption. If the vent is blocked, follow the instructions in the chapter "*Maintaining the Holding Tank Vent.*"

The most common cause of sluggish (or no) discharge in electric toilets is low voltage. Put a volt meter on *while flushing.* If it reads less than the nominal voltage (12, 24 or 32, depending upon the boat's electrical system), check the connections for corrosion, check the battery itself to see if it's getting weak, wire size to see whether it's adequate for the distance.

If the problem isn't electrical, check the joker valve; that's the first place clogs occur. If it's clean, try flushing it while you have the discharge hose off (into a pan, of course). If the problem is a clog downstream of the toilet, it'll flush just fine. If it still won't flush, the problem is in the toilet itself; the discharge impeller may be shot. Or, depending upon make/model/age, there are other possibilities that can be solved with a rebuild kit. Or maybe not; everything has a lifespan, and there does come a time when the only solution that makes any sense is a new toilet.

My toilet won't hold water. It comes in but goes right out again. What's wrong?

Nothing is wrong. Although some high-end electric toilets are designed to bring water into the bowl and hold it, manual and most electric marine toilets are not because it would end up all over the head in heavy seas. Manual toilets are designed to pull water into the bowl and push it out again with each up/down stroke. On electric toilets that have integral intake pumps (intake and discharge are all part of the same unit), the same motor that runs the integral intake pump also runs the discharge pump, so what's pulled in when you push the flush button is pulled out at the same time. When water is needed in the bowl ahead of solids, add from the sink with a cup.

Why does my bowl fill up, or partially fill, with water all by itself?

If you check the level in the bowl against the boat's waterline, I think you'll find that they're a match. That means that water outside the boat is seeking its own level inside the boat through an open through-hull, most likely the head intake through-hull. Either the wet/dry valve has failed, or someone left it in the wet position. Relying on that valve instead of closing the intake thru hull is the most common cause of boats sinking in their slips when no one is aboard to notice water flooding the cabin from under the head door. The cure: a vented loop in the toilet intake and always close the intake and discharge seacocks when preparing to leave the boat!! See the installation instructions for your toilet and also the chapter "*Installing a New Toilet and Holding Tank*" for a detailed explanation of why a vented loop in the intake is needed and how to install it correctly.

The overboard discharge hoses from the tank and toilet that go to a thru-hull via the Y-valve should never be used where we live. Do I really have to change those?

Yes...because hoses do become hard and brittle with age. The average working life of any hose is about 10 years. After that they start to deteriorate rather quickly. So any time that any hoses need replacement, replace all of them. Or, if the overboard will never be used-that seacock never opened, why not just eliminate the "Y-valves" and the hoses coming off of them to the thru-hull? If you don't regularly "exercise" that "Y-valve" and seacock and keep them both lubricated, you probably can't get them to move by now anyway if it's been more than a year or two since you've tried.

Why is my holding tank slowly backing up into the head?

Unless the holding tank is so full it's overflowing, there's no way that tank contents can back up into the toilet because the head discharge line is connected to a fitting at the *top* of the tank, and last I heard, sewage can't jump. So it isn't likely that what's backing up is coming from the tank, the problem is bowl contents aren't getting to the tank. Three possible causes are:

1. A blocked tank vent. When air in the tank displaced by incoming waste can't escape out the vent, the tank becomes pressurized, creating back pressure that won't allow flushes to get to the tank. If a blocked vent prevents air from replacing tank contents as they're pumped out, the pump or overboard discharge pump will pull a vacuum that won't allow more than about a gallon to be pulled out...in which case, your tank just might *be* full to overflowing even though you think it's been pumped out. If you've noticed that a manual toilet is getting harder to pump, or an electric toilet has started "burping" and spitting up after each flush, that's almost a guarantee that your tank vent is blocked. A new joker valve won't help.

The most common location for a vent blockage are the vent thru-hull and the vent line connection to the tank, both that end of the hose and the fitting on the tank. The cure: Clean out the vent thru-hull and the vent line connection to the tank.

2. The toilet discharge hose runs up and over a loop (not necessarily a *vented* loop), or it's just an uphill run from the toilet to the tank inlet fitting...and since water runs downhill, that's what it's doing because you aren't flushing in the dry mode long enough to push the flush over the top of the loop or get the flush to the tank. A new joker valve may prevent the back flow from making it into the bowl, but only for a short time...until enough flushes stretches the slit open. However, joker valves in manual toilets should be replaced annually, or at least every two years, because they're essential to the efficient operation of the toilet. Read the chapter *"Flush With Success"* for the explanation of what a joker valve really does. The cure: learn to flush longer in the dry mode. Few people realize that any manual toilet that's working anywhere *near* factory spec can move bowl contents up to 6 linear or 4 vertical feet in the dry mode. Learning how to use the dry mode to do more than just push the flush out of sight can increase the number of flushes your tank can hold by up to 50%.

3. A blockage in the head discharge hose...either sea water mineral buildup in it has reduced the diameter enough to all but block it, or somebody flushed something they shouldn't have.

4. A combination of any or all of the above.

What is a joker valve?

A joker valve is a one-way valve—a cup-shaped rubber piece that has a slit in the bottom, a "duckbill," and a flange that acts as the gasket between the toilet discharge hose fitting and the toilet base. Because the slit and "duckbill" become stretched with use, the joke valve should be replace annually, or at least every two years. See the chapter *"Maintaining Marine Toilets"* for more information about joker valves and their functions.

Do I need a strainer in my toilet intake line?

If you're sucking up weeds and other animal or vegetable sea life, you need a strainer-not only on the toilet intake, but on the engine intake too. If that's not a problem, you don't need one.

part VII

COMMON PROBLEMS AND SOLUTIONS

Although I totally concur with those who choose to replace a Jabsco manual pump instead of rebuilding it, rebuilding a toilet does **not** have to be an "icky" job. It's only an icky job if:

    a) You don't do it as scheduled preventive maintenance-which you get to do on your terms at your convenience-resulting in the need for a repair, which you never get to do on your terms when it's convenient. It's called *preventive* maintenance because it prevents the need for 99% of repairs. An "icky job" is the price you pay for neglecting it.

    b) Even if you do decide to rebuild before neglect leads to catastrophic failure, you don't take the time to prep for the job before taking anything apart. Preparation is 90% of the key to the success of any job.

Prepping to rebuild a toilet starts with thoroughly rinsing out the pump and plumbing-the whole system-with plenty of clean water before taking anything apart. Put plastic garbage bags or disposable aluminum pans under hose connections to catch any spills. (Warming hoses with a blow dryer makes them easier to remove and replace).

Have a couple rolls of paper shop towels (super heavy duty paper towels, all I've ever seen are blue) handy...you'll need them.

Every rebuild or "service" kit includes a copy of the parts list with exploded drawing. If it's missing, download and print one from the manufacturer's website. That drawing is the only "instructions" you'll get, so keep it close at hand and refer to it. Use the camera in your phone to take photos of the parts you're replacing while they're still in place and compare them with the drawings to make sure you get the new part oriented correctly and/or installed in the right order if you had to remove more than one at a time.

Finally, put a healthy squirt of thick teflon or silicon grease (SuperLube, available from Ace Hardware is the best choice) into the pump to lube the toilet last thing before you put it back on the base. *(See "Lubricating a Manual Toilet" in the chapter "Maintaining Marine Toilets" for more details)*

When putting the discharge fitting back on the pump after replacing the joker valve, be careful not to over-tighten the bolts/screws. The flange on the joker valve (which, by the way, should align vertically) is the gasket that seals the fitting connection to the pump body. You want that connection to be leak proof, but over-tightening the screws/bolts will put puckers in the flange, actually causing it to leak. So start by tightening all the screws just enough to barely achieve a snug connection, then only a quarter turn or even less of all the screws is necessary close off a leak.

1. Visit the pump-out station in your marina (and others that you're likely to use) before you'll need a pump-out to find out whether their adapter at the end of the pump-out hose will fit the deck pump-out fitting on your boat. If it doesn't (or even if it does because you may need it at another pump-out), you'll have to furnish your own.

Your best choice is a SeaLand "Nozall Pump-out Adapter," available from most marine products retailers. It provides an airtight seal between the pump-out station nozzle and most boats' waste deck pump-out fittings. Because it's available in three sizes you'll need to measure the inside diameter of the your deck pump-out fitting and count the number of threads per inch (tpi) to make sure you order the one that fits your boat.

SeaLand Nozall
PumpoutAdapter
Photo courtesy of Dometic/Sealand

2. Before you arrive at the pump out station, locate the deck fitting cap labeled "waste." In some marinas, this can determine which side of the boat you put next to the dock. Also make sure you have the key to open it handy.

3. Once you've arrived at the pump out station, tie off the boat to the dock, and make sure both ends of the boat are tied off tightly; you don't want either end to swing away from the dock! Be sure you dock as close to the pump-out as possible because their hoses are often not very long.

4. Once you're sure the boat is secure, take the key up to the deck fitting cap and carefully open it. Before you open the cap, it's always a good idea to have a hose handy to rinse off any tank contents or drips from the pump-out hose. If you suspect the holding tank is extremely full, open it only a quarter turn to relieve any pressure without a spew. If there is a spew, it's because the tank is pressurized—a sure sign that the tank vent is blocked, in which case the vent must be cleared before attempting to pump out!

5. Once you can remove the cap, do so being careful to hang onto it. Unlike fuel and water deck fittings, waste pump-out fittings do not have a chain that attaches the cap to the fitting to prevent the cap from going overboard. Do not set the cap down next to the deck fitting or anywhere that could allow it to slide overboard due to rocking or carelessness! Put it in your pocket or in the cockpit or anywhere it can't fall in.

6. Now you're ready to pump out the tank. Get off the boat and stand on the dock to attach the pump-out hose. If this is your first time, ask the dock hand for help to do this. Do not just walk away and leave things in the dock hand's hands once pump-out has started. Instead, keep a close eye on the clear sight glass at the end of the pump-out hose to make sure the pump is actually pulling out waste—and continues to pull it out until the tank is empty. To be sure, check your tank level monitor or visually inspect the tank if you don't have a monitor.

If you stop seeing anything moving through the sight glass after only a few seconds, _cease pump-out immediately!_ That's an indication that the tank vent is blocked; allowing the pump-out to keep pulling against a blocked vent can result in an imploded tank. Do not attempt to pump-out again or use the toilet(s) again until you've cleared the vent.

7. Once the tank is empty, disconnect the pump-out hose and put a gallon or two of water into the tank via the deck pump-out fitting—because that sends the water into the tank at the bottom where it can stir up any sludge and hold it in suspension so it can be pumped out. Reconnect the pump-out to remove the water. Do this twice.

Remove your own adapter and rinse it off, rinse any drips or spills off your boat, put the cap back on the deck fitting...and you're done.

CLEANING UP FROM A SEWAGE SPILL

Before you start, buy a gallon of PureAyre, available from Amazon, pet supply stores or directly from the company. *(See more details about this product in the "Bilges" section of "Boat Odors Are Not All In Your Head")* Any version will work equally well. I'd also buy a good quality 1 gallon garden pump sprayer jug (you **could** use a trigger sprayer, but your hand will get very tired).

You cannot eliminate any odor unless you first eliminate the source of that odor! So first you must clean up the spill completely, using only detergent and water, and maybe a scrub brush or even a power washer, but **no** bleach!! Be sure to clean every surface, nook and cranny in the affected area.

After you're sure you've cleaned up every bit of the spill with plenty of detergent and water, remove all the excess water with a shop vac, sponge and bucket, whatever works. When everything is pretty much dry-no more than just damp-lightly coat every surface, nook and cranny in the affected area with the PureAyre. **Do not rinse!** Just let it dry, leaving all hatches open-even turn a fan on if you can-for at least 24 hours. If you still have any odor, you missed a spot.

Use PureAyre to eliminate residual odors left in lockers by permeated hoses after you've replaced them. If cushions or other soft goods were affected, clean them and then saturate (not dripping wet...just enough sprayed into the foam from both sides to penetrate to the middle of the cushion) with PureAyre, then leave outside in the sunshine to dry all day.

That will get rid of the odor permanently. If you still have odor after you've closed everything up again, you missed a spot.

And by the way, PureAyre is safe for use around children and pets...and food. So it's also the best way to get rid of residual odors (the meat that spoiled when the power to the fridge died, the sandwiches you forgot to take out of the cooler) in bait boxes, refrigerators and iceboxes, musty wet lockers and anywhere else that stinks. It's also the only product I've found that eliminates diesel odors—after you've cleaned up that spill!

THE MOST COMMON TOILET PROBLEMS AND PROBABLE CURES

(The following are generic solutions to the most common problems. If you need more information specific to your make/model/age toilet, see your owners' manual or contact the manufacturer's tech support team.)

Toilet doesn't bring in any flush water
Make sure inlet seacock is open
Check for barnacle or other blockage in the inlet thru-hull
Check inlet hose for mineral buildup (requires removing the hose from the pump)

Manual toilets
Make sure wet/dry lever is in the "wet" position

Electric toilet
Replace worn out or failed intake impeller

Water fills bowl when not in use
Manual or electric raw water toilets
Close inlet seacock
Install vented loop in intake (see chapter 2 *"Installing a New Toilet and Holding Tank"* for instructions

Pressurized fresh water toilets
Repair or replace inlet water valve

Manual toilet is hard to pump
Pump needs lubrication (see chapter 3 *"Maintaining Marine Toilets"* for instructions)
Holding tank vent is blocked (see chapter 3 *"Maintaining the Holding Tank Vent"* for explanation)
Mineral buildup in toilet discharge hose creating partial blockage

Sluggish discharge or toilet "burps" and flush returns to bowl, or toilet "spits up."
Make sure discharge seacock is open (only in waters where it's legal to flush directly over board)

Worn out joker valve. (See "Joker Valves 101" in chapter 3)

Blocked holding tank vent (see chapter 3 *"Maintaining the Holding Tank Vent"* for explanation and cure)

Mineral buildup in toilet discharge hose creating partial blockage (see chapter 3 for cure)

Check for clog in discharge line creating back pressure

Electric toilet
Low voltage to toilet motor—use a volt meter while flushing to check.

Problem	Possible Cause	Service Instruction
1. Water will not stay in bowl	a. Loose clamp ring b. Improper seal around flush ball due to dirt or debris on flush ball or under flush ball seal c. Worn or damaged seal d. Worn or damaged flush ball	a. Tighten clamp ring adjustment nut b. Inspect flush ball for foreign debris. Clean flush ball and underside of seal if needed c. Replace seal d. Replace flush ball
2. Plastic flush ball will not close completely	a. Too much friction between flush ball and ball seal b. Water valve screws are too tight c. Defective spring cartridge	a. Lubricate between flush ball and ball seal with furniture polish or cooking spray b. Loosen screws lightly c. Check spring tension by pushing flush lever down, then release it suddenly. If lever does not snap back into position, replace spring cartridge
3. Flush ball will not open	a. Broken shaft b. Shaft not full engaged in the spring cartridge	a. Replace shaft b. Put pressure on shaft from under the flush ball (pushing into spring cartridge) until it engages. You may have to rotate flush ball until shaft lines up with square in spring cartridge
4. Water does not shut off in toilet overflows)	a. Not enough clearance between pedal and top of water valve cap b. Dirt lodged in water valve seal	a. Adjust cam strap so clearance is .06 in (1.5mm) max b. Disassemble, clean water valve
5. Water does not enter toilet bowl properly	a. Insufficient water flow rate at toilet b. Water valve clogged c. Plugged rim wash holes in toilet	a. Check water flow rate at toilet. Rate should be 2 gpm (7.6 lpm) b. Remove and clean screen located at inlet of water valve c. Clean holes. If still a problem, replace the toilet bowl
6. Lifting foot pedal does not add water to the bowl	a. Too much clearance between pedal and top of water valve	a. Adjust cam strap so clearance is .06 in (1.5mm) max
7. Water leaking from water valve	a. Water valve body cracked due to freeze damage b. Water line connection is loose or not sealing properly c. Defective water valve d. Stripped threads	a. Replace water valve b. Insure that threads are not cross-threaded and tighten c. Replace water valve d. Replace water valve
8. Water leaking from rear of toilet bowl	a. Worn or defective vacuum breaker b. Loose vacuum breaker or hose clamp c. Cracked or defective toilet bowl	a. Remove cap (if applicable) from vacuum breaker. Flush. If water leaks during flush, vacuum breaker needs replaced b. Secure vacuum breaker connection c. Replace toilet bowl
9. Water is leaking from the base/toilet connection	a. Clamp ring may be loose b. Ball seals may be worn or defective	a. Remove pedestal cover and tighten the clamp ring b. Replace the ball seals
10. Vacuum pump running too often between flushes	a. Water leaks out of bowl between flush ball and ball seal b. Vacuum line leak	a. Leave small amount of water in bowl. If water is sucked from bowl, see problem 1 and 2 b. Tighten all connections at toilet, vacuum generator toilet or vacuum holding tank (incl hose clamps and threaded spin nuts). If leak persists, contact Customer Service
11. Vacuum pump will not shut off	a. A vacuum leak exists b. Insufficient vacuum (pump creates less than 10 inches Hg) c. Faulty vacuum switch (pump creates more than 10 inches Hg) d. Improper vacuum generator wiring e. Bellows not pumping	a. See problem 9b b. Isolate pump and use vacuum gauge to check vacuum levels. Could be a plugged discharge line or worn duckbill valves c. Replace vacuum switch d. Refer to writing diagram to check fpr proper wiring e. Tighten set screw in eccentric to motor shaft if needed. Check for damage to bellows and motor shaft. Replace if necessary.
12. Vacuum pump will not run ⚡ ⚠	a. No electrical power b. Loose or broken electrical wiring c. Improper electrical connections d. Faulty vacuum switch e. Faulty motor f. Shut-down relay prevents pumping	a. Check input power, circuit break and fuse b. Tighten o reconnect wires at vacuum pump and tank, vacuum generator, or vacuum holding tank c. Make certain wires at vacuum switch are connected at "B" terminals d. To check vacuum switch, short across "B" terminals with jumper wire e. Replace motor f. Empty the holding tank
13. Vacuum pump is running too slow, overheating, blowing fuses or circuit breaker ⚡ ⚠	a. Gear motor is worn, defective b. Plugged vent line or vent filter c. Blockage in discharge line d. Improper wire size e. Improper voltage f. Vacuum pump bellows clogged with tissue	a. Check motor; replace if needed. b. Disassemble and clean out vent line. Replace vent filter if necessary. c. Disassemble and clean discharge line. Be certain that in-line valves (duckbill) and seacock are in proper position d. Wire size too small. Check electrical diagram for proper wire size for voltage of pump e. Check input power for low voltage f. Remove and clean bellows assembly (When flushing toilet, using more water may alleviate this problem)
14. Toilet will not flush (no vacuum) See problem 15 if necessary. ⚡	a. Blockage exists in the system. b. Pump will not run. c. Duckbill valves in vacuum pump are inverted due to blocked discharge line or an attempt to pump out against closed seacock	a. Open flush ball, check 1 inch (25mm) orifice at bottom of base for blockage and dislodge it. If blockage is not in base, it may be found in: • outlet of vacuum tank • inlet of vacuum generator • diptube of vacuum generator • inlet of vacuum pump b. See problem 12. c. Replace duckbill valves, making sure they point in the correct direction.
15. Blockage between toilet and vacuum generator	a. Collapsed vacuum line b. Sharp bends or kinks in vacuum hose c. Improper operation of toilet d. Foreign objects were flushed down the toilet	a. Inspect vacuum line for collapsed condition; replace if needed. b. Inspect vacuum hose for kinks or bends. If less than 8.5 inches (216mm) radius on any bend, reposition hose. c. Make sure each person using toilet knows correct procedure. d. DO NOT flush any non-dissolving item or excessive tissue.
16. Pump emits odor ⚡	a. Loose or defective hose connection on pump b. Loose intake or discharge fittings on pump c. Worn, torn, or punctured pumps bellows (vac generator) or diaphragm (vac holding tank)	a. Tighten connection or replace hose and make new connection b. Tighten intake or discharge fittings on pump. Replace nipples or adapters if necessary. c. Replace pump bellows or diaphragm.

Appendix A

MOST POPULAR EQUIPMENT
WITH PARTS LISTS
AND EXPLODED DRAWINGS

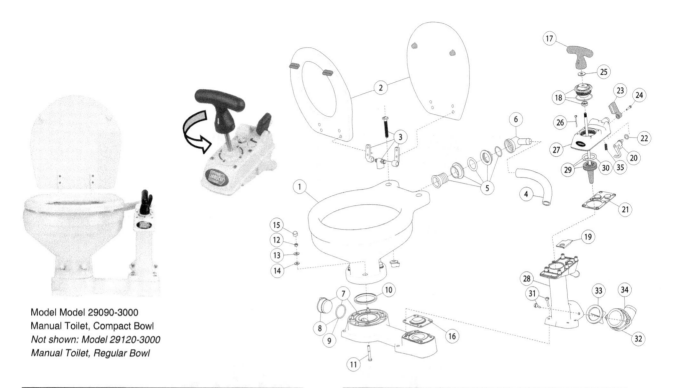

Model Model 29090-3000
Manual Toilet, Compact Bowl
Not shown: Model 29120-3000
Manual Toilet, Regular Bowl

Key	Description	Qty Per Toilet	Part No	A	B	C	D	E
1	BOWL COMPACT TOILET	1	29096-0000					
	BOWL REGULAR TOILET	1	29126-0000					
2	SEAT, LID & HINGE SET	1						
	COMPACT TOILET		29097-1000					
	REGULAR TOILET		29127-1000					
3	HINGE SET (1 PAIR)	1						
	COMPACT TOILET		29098-1000					
	REGULAR TOILET		29098-2000					
4	HOSE COMPACT TOILET	1	29035-1000					
	HOSE REGULAR TOILET	1	29035-1001					
5	INTAKE SEAL +	1	29048-0000					
6	INTAKE ELBOW							
7	BASE, PLUG + O-RING ASSY	1	29041-1000					
8	PLUG + O-RING ASSY	1						
	(UP TO 2002 – SCREW)		29028-1000					
	(FROM 2003 – BAYONET)		29028-2000					
9	O-RING (PLUG)	1	–					
10	O-RING (BOWL)	1	–					1
11	BOLT (S/S)	4	–					4
12	NUT (S/S)	4	–					4
13	WASHER (S/S)	4	–					4
14	WASHER (NYLON)	4	–					4
15	CAP	4	–	2				4
16	BASE VALVE GASKET	1	29043-0000	1	1		1	
17	HANDLE	1			1	1		
18	SEAL HOUSING ASSY	1		1	1	1		
	(UP TO 1997)		29044-0000					
	(1998 TO 2007)		29044-2000					
	(FROM 2008)		29044-3000					

Repair Kits Available

Kit	Part No	Description
A	29045-0000	SERVICE KIT (UP TO 1997)
A	29045-2000	SERVICE KIT (FROM 1998 T0 2007)
A	29045-3000	SERVICE KIT (FROM 2008)
B	29040-3000	PUMP ASSEMBLY
C	29094-3000	VALVE COVER ASSEMBLY
D	29051-2000	PUMP CYLINDER ASSEMBLY
E	29047-0000	BASE TO BOWL MOUNTING KIT

Key	Description	Qty Per Toilet	Part No	A	B	C	D	E
19	TOP VALVE SEAT	1	–		1	1	1	1
20	CAM	1	–		1	1		
21	TOP VALVE GASKET	1	29042-0000	1	1			
22	O-RING (FLUSH LEVER)	1	–	1	1	1		
23	FLUSH CONTROL LEVER	1	–		1	1		
24	SCREW (FLUSH LEVER)	1	–	1	1	1		
25	BUFFER	1	–	1	1			
26	SCREW (VALVE COVER)	6	–	1	6	6	1	
27	VALVE COVER	1	–		1	1		
28	PUMP CYLINDER	1	–		1		1	
29	PISTON, ROD & O-RING ASSY	1	29046-3000		1			
30	O-RING (PISTON)	1	–	1	1			
31	SCREW (PUMP CYLINDER)	6	–	1	3		3	
32	DISCHARGE FLANGE	1	29091-1000		1		1	
33	JOKER VALVE	1	29092-1000	1	1		1	
34	DISCHARGE ELBOW	1	29029-1000		1		1	
35	VALVE SPRING (ONLY FROM 1998)	1	–	1	1	1	1	

GROCO

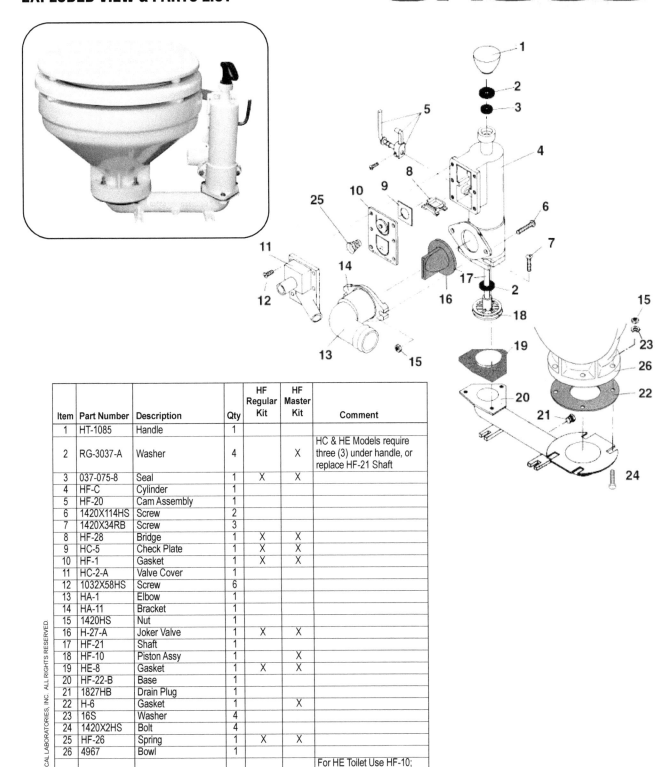

Item	Part Number	Description	Qty	HF Regular Kit	HF Master Kit	Comment
1	HT-1085	Handle	1			
2	RG-3037-A	Washer	4		X	HC & HE Models require three (3) under handle, or replace HF-21 Shaft
3	037-075-8	Seal	1	X	X	
4	HF-C	Cylinder	1			
5	HF-20	Cam Assembly	1			
6	1420X114HS	Screw	2			
7	1420X34RB	Screw	3			
8	HF-28	Bridge	1	X	X	
9	HC-5	Check Plate	1	X	X	
10	HF-1	Gasket	1	X	X	
11	HC-2-A	Valve Cover	1			
12	1032X58HS	Screw	6			
13	HA-1	Elbow	1			
14	HA-11	Bracket	1			
15	1420HS	Nut	1			
16	H-27-A	Joker Valve	1	X	X	
17	HF-21	Shaft	1			
18	HF-10	Piston Assy	1		X	
19	HE-8	Gasket	1	X	X	
20	HF-22-B	Base	1			
21	1827HB	Drain Plug	1			
22	H-6	Gasket	1		X	
23	16S	Washer	4			
24	1420X2HS	Bolt	4			
25	HF-26	Spring	1	X	X	
26	4967	Bowl	1			
NS	HC-10	Piston Assy	1		NLA	For HE Toilet Use HF-10; Replace HF-21 shaft also or use three (3) RG-3037-A beneath handle
NS	HT-49-A	Vacuum Breaker Assy	1			Sold Separately
NS	TC-50	Seat	1			
NS	H-7	Bowl Elbow	1			

NS = NOT SHOWN

© 1999 GROSS MECHANICAL LABORATORIES, INC. ALL RIGHTS RESERVED.

BOWL TYPE	A	B	C	D	E	F
MARINE	13 (330)	24 3/4 (629)	10 3/8 (264)	17 1/4 (438)	17 3/4 (451)	6 1/2 (165)
HOUSEHOLD	13 1/8 (334)	27 7/8 (708)	11 1/2 (292)	20 (508)	18 1/4 (464)	7 (179)

INCHES
(MM)

NOTE:
1. THE SEAT WILL OPEN WITHIN THE DEPTH OF THE BOWL (D), HOWEVER, IT MAY BE DESIRABLE TO INCREASE THIS ANGLE BY ALLOWING MORE ROOM AT THE BACK OF THE BOWL FOR THE SEAT TO OPEN.
2. DIMENSIONS ARE FOR REFERENCE AS VITREOUS CHINA DIMENSIONS MAY VARY +/- 5%.

ITEM #	PART#	DESCRIPTION
1	25101	Base
2	25102	Base Drain Plug
3	25103	Base Drain Plug O-Ring Seal*
4	25104	Base Mounting Hole Plugs (4)
5	25105	Bowl Gasket O Ring*
6	F081	Bowl Bolt 1/4' - 20 X 2" S/S Hex Head (4)
7	RNI	Nylon Shoulder Washer (4)*
8	1226B	Nut: 1/4"-20 S/S (4)
9	VCAP	Vinyl Cap (4)*
10	221300	Vacuum Breaker Assembly
11	221356	BSP Nut
12	25310	BSP Nut: O Ring*
13	168006	Cover, Vacuum Breaker Assembly
14	PLH-50P	Hose, 1/2"
15	25215	Inlet Valve Lever
16	25300	Inlet Vavle Assembly
17	F409	Screw:Phil. Thread-Forming, #8 X 1" S/S (2)
18	25310	Inlet Valve Bracket
19	F403	Screw:Phil. Thread-Forming,#8 X 1/2" S/S (6)
20	25220	Discharge Pump Flush Handle
22	F408	Screw: 1/4"-20 X 5/8", S/S (4)
23	1228F	Flapper Valve*
24	25212	Discharge Elbow
25	25213	Joker Valve*

ITEM #	PART#	DESCRIPTION
26	25216	Joker Valve Hose Clamp (Small)
27	25217	Joker Valve Hose Clamp (Large)
28	25214	Pump Cover
29	25200	Pump Assembly
30	25201	Pump Base
31	25202	Pump Top
32	25203	Diaphragm Piston
33	25204	Diaphragm Piston Cap
34	25206	Discharge Shut Off Seal*
35	227015	Diaphragm*
36	25207	Piston Lever SS
37	F149VT	Socket Set Screw
38	25208	Clevis Pin
39	1210B	Cotter Pin, Rue Ring (3)
40	F400	Screw: #8-32 X 5/8" S/S (6)
41	F401	Screw: #8-32 X 3/4" S/S
42	F402	Nut: #8-32 S/S (7)
43	F404	Washer: 1/4" Flat S/S
44	F405	Lock Washer: 1/4" Split S/S
45	1124	Screw: 1/4-20 x 1/2" S/S
47	25209	Piston Shaft
48	25210	Shut Off Lever
49	25211	Shut Off Lever Pin

* = Included in 2500RK Repair Kit

RARITAN
The Most Dependable Name on the Water

BOWL & SEAT

1236AW	Spud Assembly	
1237W	Marine-Size Bowl Assembly	
1244W	White Household-Style Bowl Assembly	
1238A	Marine-Size Seat & Cover	
1245	White Household-Style Seat & Cover	

NOT SHOWN:

25306	Inlet Diaphragm*
25307	Plunger O-ring*

* = Included in 2500RK Repair Kit

MANUAL TOILET MODEL PH II & PHE II PARTS LIST

Part No.	Description
1115	3/8"-16 x 1 1/2" Hex Head S/S Bolt(2)
1124	1/4"- 20 x 1/2" R.H. Machine Screw
1200CW	Pump Housing
1201	Intake and Discharge Valve Ball (2)
1202	Intake and Discharge Valve Gasket (2)
1203BW	Intake Valve Body w/"O" Rings (1203B, 1203B1, 1203B2, 1203B3)
1203W	Air Valve Assembly
1204B	Intake Valve Cap
1206W	Handle
1209BW	Valve Handle
1210	Handle Socket
1210A	Cotter Pin (4)
1211PL	Piston Rod Yoke
1212W	Piston Rod Assembly w/"O" Ring (1232MS)
1213W	Piston Rod Seal Assembly, Pre-6/92, (Incl. 1213A, B, C, D)
1213A	"U" Cup Seal (Pre-6/92)
1213B	Delrin Washer (Pre-6/92)
1213C	Snap Ring (Pre-6/92)
1213D	White Neoprene Washer (Pre-6/92)
1214W	Piston Shaft Seal Cartridge Assy (1214,1214A, 1214B) Fits pumps mfg. after 6/92
1216	Clevis Pin (3)
1217	Discharge Valve Cap
1218	Fulcrum Link (2)
1222AW	90° Discharge w/Flange (Std.)
1222B	Straight Discharge (Opt.)
1223B	Flange Nut 3/8"-16 S/S (2)
1226	Housing Screw 1/4"-20 x 1" S/S (4)
1226B	Nut, 1/4"-20 S/S (8)
1228CW	Flapper Valve Assembly (1/2" Holes)
1232MS	Piston "O" Ring
1234	Bowl Gasket
1236E	Bowl Elbow
1246W	Base Cover (2 pcs.)
1248W	Base w/Plug
1249	Base Plug
1250W	Base and Cover Assy.(1246W and1248W)
C253	Joker Valve
CH42	Hose (¾" I.D.)
CH43P	Hose Clamp (2)
F005	1/4"- 20 x 5/16" S/S Socket Set Screw
F081	Bowl Bolt 1/4"-20 x 2 S/S Hex head
LWS	Intake and Discharge Valve Spring (2)
RNI	Nylon Shoulder Washer

PARTS FOR ELECTRIC DRIVE

Part No.	Part Name
1100W	Gear Box Housing Assembly
1102	Worm
1104	Ball Bearing
1105	Snap Ring
1106AS	Rubber Connection w/Sleeve
1106W	Coupling w/Sleeve, complete
1108A	Motor Mounting Nut (2)
1109*	Motor (12, 24, 32, 120V DC)
1110	"O" Ring
1112	Link
1113	Link Pin, Worm Gear Pin
1115	3/8" - 16 x 1 1/2" Hex Head S/S Bolt
1115A	3/8" - 16 Hex Jam Nut S/S
1116BW	Connecting Rod Assy. (1116B, 1114B, 1114D)

The PHII is a manually operated double action piston toilet. The PHII can be converted to its electrical counterpart by adding an electrical conversion kit part# PHECKII*

The PHEII is the electric version which incorporates an electric motor driven gear box.

Part No.	Description
1117B	Crank Bolt
1118	Lock Washer (4)
1119/1119A	Hex Head Screw (4)
1120W	Worm Gear Assy.(1111, 1113, 1120)
1122	"O" Ring
1123	Gear Box Cover
1124	1/4"- 20 x 1/2" R.H. Machine Screw(4)
M23A	#10 Lockwasher S/S (2)

PHC PARTS

Part No.	Description
1226A	Housing Screw 1/4"-20 x 1 1/4" S/S (4)
1226C	Plastic Spacer Washer (4)
1301PW	Toilet Base Assembly (1301P, 1343)
F081	Bowl Bolt 1/4"- 20 x 2" S/S Hex head

RARITAN INSTALLATION ACCESSORIES

Part No.	Description
163000	In-Line Strainer
164000	Push button switch
1PCP22	C.P., Cleans Potties, Bio-enzymatic, 22 oz.
CHTII	Compact holding tank - 5 gallon
CON22	Concentrate 22 oz. bottle
SH	Sanitation Hose (sold by the foot)
SL	Super Lube 1/2 oz. tube
TWK	Toilet Water Marine Head Disinfectant Kit
VL 3/4	Vented Loop 3/4"
VL 1 1/2	Vented Loop 1 1/2"
YV	"Y" Valve

BOWL & SEAT

Part No.	Description
1236AW	Spud assy.
1237W	Marine-size Bowl assy.
1244W	White Household-style Bowl assy.
1238A	Marine-size seat & cover
1245	Household-style seat & cover
VCAP	Vinyl Cap

OVERHAUL KITS

Part No.	Description
PHRKII	PHII&PHEII-U-cup Seal (mfg.before6/92)
PHRKIIC	PHII&PHEII-Cartridge Seal (mfg.after 6/92)
PHIIPUMP	PHII Pump replacement assembly

*Specify Voltage

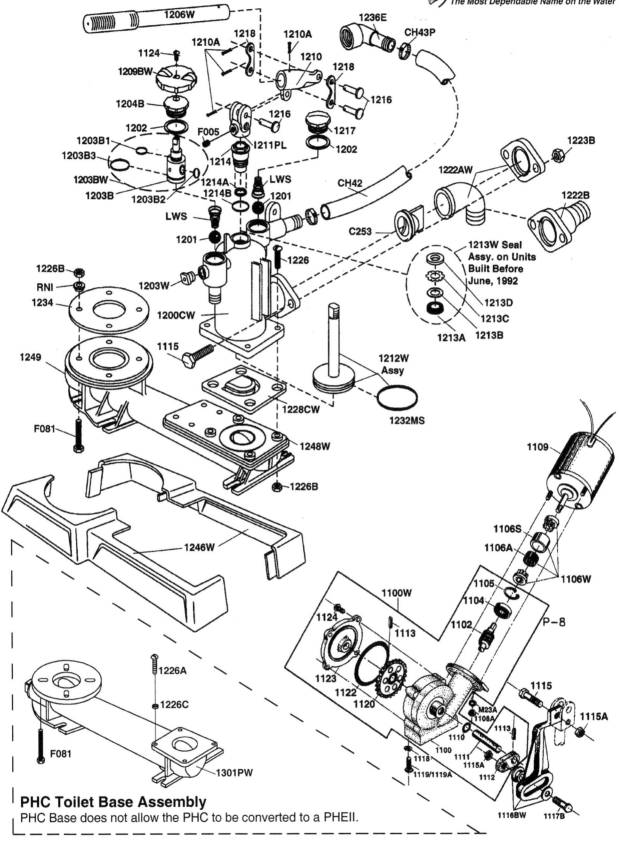

PHC Toilet Base Assembly
PHC Base does not allow the PHC to be converted to a PHEII.

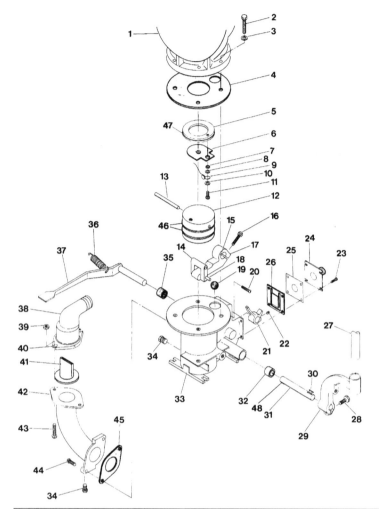

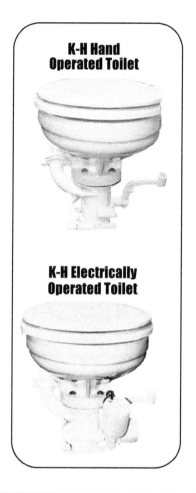

K-H Hand Operated Toilet

K-H Electrically Operated Toilet

Item	Part Number	Description	Qty	Model K Regular Kit		Item	Part Number	Description	Qty	Model K Regular Kit
1	4985-0	Bowl (White color)	1			28	51618x1 HB	Bolt	1	
	4985-1	Bowl (Bone color)				29	HT-3560- D	Arm	1	
	4985-2	Bowl (Grey color)				30, 31	HT-6566-K	Shaft	1	
2	51618x2 HB	Bolts	4			30, 48	KS	Key Set	1	
3	20LP	Washers	4			32	WS-2422	Seal	1	x
4	HT-52- A	Gasket	1	x		33	K-A	Pump Housing	1	
5	K-4	Plate	1			34	1827 HB	Drain Plug	2	
6-7	HT-26- A	Gasket	1	x		35	HT-3564	Seal	1	x
8-11	HT-84- A	Spring Assembly	1	x		36	S-72587	Spring	1	
12-18	K-32	Piston & Crank	1			37	HT-3570- A	Pedal	1	
12	K-92	Piston & Rings	1			38	HA-1	Discharge	1	
13	K-3-P	Piston Pin	1			40	HA-11	Bracket	1	
14-18	K-2	Crank Assembly	1			41	H-27- A	Joker Valve	1	x
19	HT-56	Check Ball	1	x		42	K-8	Discharge	1	
20	1024X1 RB	Screw	1			45	K-7- A	Gasket	1	x
21-22	K-1	Cam	1			46	K-3- R	Piston Rings Set (2)	1	x
23	1024x12 HB	Screws	4			47	2-041	O-Ring	1	x
24	HT-3556	Inlet	1			NS	500- D-0	Seat (White color)	1	
25	HT-3557- A	Gasket	1	x			500- D-1	Seat (Bone color)		
26	HT-3557	Gasket	1	x			500- D-2	Seat (Grey color)		
27	HT-3560- C	Handle	1			NS	TT-50 NLA	Seat for 4978 bowl	1	

THE *NEW* GET RID OF BOAT ODORS

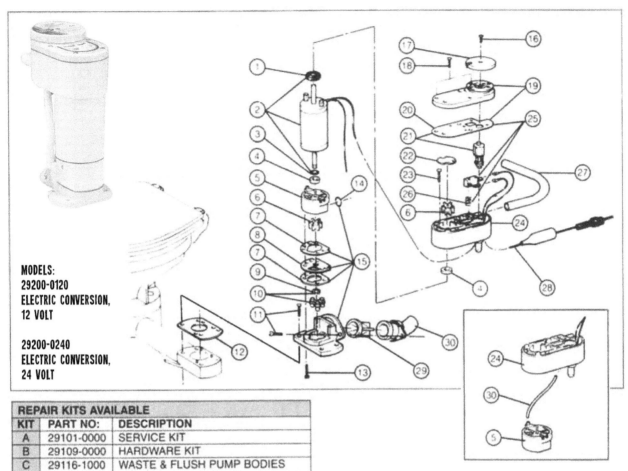

MODELS:
29200-0120
ELECTRIC CONVERSION,
12 VOLT

29200-0240
ELECTRIC CONVERSION,
24 VOLT

REPAIR KITS AVAILABLE

KIT	PART NO:	DESCRIPTION
A	29101-0000	SERVICE KIT
B	29109-0000	HARDWARE KIT
C	29116-1000	WASTE & FLUSH PUMP BODIES

KEY	DESCRIPTION		QTY PER TOILET	PART NO:	A	B	C
1	SLINGER (LARGE)		1				
2	MOTOR	12V	1	29108-0120			
	ASSEMBLY	24V	1	29108-0240			
3	SLINGER (SMALL)		1		1		
4	SEAL		2		2		2
5	WASTE PUMP BODY		1				1
6	IMPELLER		2		2		
7	GASKET (PAPER)		2		2	2	2
8	WEARPLATE (STAINLESS STEEL)		1			1	
9	SPRING WASHER		1		1		
10	CHOPPER + SPRING WASHER		1	29102-1000			
11	MOUNTING SCREW (PAR)		-		1		1
12	BASE GASKET (RUBBER)		1	29072-1000			
13	SCREW (WASTE PUMP)		4			4	
14	O-RING		1		1		1
15	MACERATOR HOUSING		1	29071-1000			

KEY	DESCRIPTION	QTY PER TOILET	PART NO:	A	B	C
16	SCREW (CONTROL KNOB)	1		1	1	1
17	CONTROL KNOB	1	29077-1000			
18	SCREW (FLUSH PUMP COVER)	7		1	7	1
19	FLUSH PUMP COVER ASSY	1	29061-1000			
20	FLUSH PUMP GASKET (CORK)	1	29075-1000	1		1
21	CONTROL VALVE ASSY	1	29083-1000			
22	WEARPLATE (BRASS)	1			1	
23	SCREW (FLUSH PUMP)	2		1	2	1
24	FLUSH PUMP BODY	1				1
25	SWITCH ASSY	1	29103-1000	1		
26	SWITCH SPRING	1				1
27	HOSE (ALL TOILETS)	1	29035-1000			
28	CABLE ASSY (WITHOUT FUSE)	1	29106-1000			
29	JOKER VALVE	1	29092-0000			
30	BLEED HOSE	1	29019-1010	1		1
31	PUMPGUARD (NOT SHOWN)	1	36220-0000			

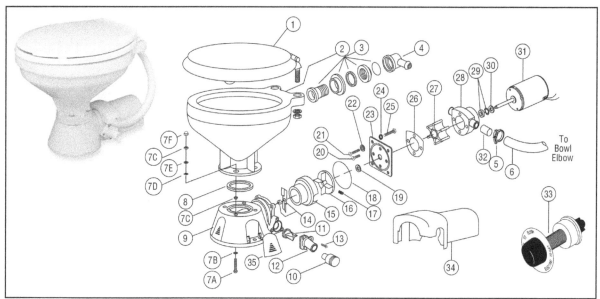

To
Bowl
Elbow

PARTS LIST

Key	Description	Qty. Req.	Part Number
1	Seat & Cover, Compact Size	1	18753-0437
	Seat & Cover, Household Size	1	18753-0438
2	Bowl, Compact Size	1	59127-7002
	Bowl, Household Size	1	18753-0060
3 & 4	Bowl Spud & Intake Elbow & O-ring	1	29048-0000
5	Clamp	1	18753-0044
6	Hose	1	29035-0001
7	Bowl Installation Hardware	1	18753-0637
7A	Phillips Head Screw**	4	
7B	Washer, Starlock**	4	
7C	Hex Nut** (two places)	4	
7D	Washer, Plastic**	4	
7E	Washer Stainless steel**	8	
7F	Nut Cap**	4	
8	O-Ring Bowl/Seal	1	44101-1000
9	Base Assembly**	1	37004-1000
10	1-1/2" Adaptor, Discharge Port	1	98023-0080
11	Joker Valve* **	1	
12	1" Discharge Port**	1	44107-1300
13	Screw**	3	
14	Chopper Plate† with Lock Nut	1	37056-1000
15	Macerator Housing †	1	37014-0000
16	Centrifugal Impeller †	1	37006-0000
17	Set Screw †	1	18753-0492
18	O-ring*†	1	43990-0066
19	Sealing Sleeve †	1	37036-1000
20	Screw †	2	91009-0096
21	Screw †	2	91010-0130
22	Washer, Fiber*†	2	35445-0000
23	Wearplate Kit ‡†	1	37018-0000
24	Lock Washer #10, Stainless Kit †	4	
25	Screw †	4	91027-0011
26	Gasket*†	1	12558-0000
27	Flexible Impeller*†	1	6303-0003
28	Body †	1	12554-0000
29	Seal & Retainer*†	1	1040-0000

Key	Description	Qty. Req.	Part Number
30	Slinger †	1	6342-0000
31	Motors:		
	Motor - 12 Volt EMC †	1	37064-0000
	Motor - 24 Volt EMC†	1	37065-0000
32	Adaptor	2	93003-0240
33	Switch & Plate	1	37020-0000
34	Motor Cover †	1	43990-0051
35	Screw Cover (3 each)	1	37003-1000
	Service Kit		37040-0000
	Motor/Pump Assy. 12V EMC †		37041-0010
	Motor/Pump Assy. 24V EMC †		37042-0011

* Parts Supplied with Service Kit 37040-0000.

** Parts included with base 37004-1000.

‡ Wearplate #23 includes Sealing Sleeve #19 and Pump/Base O-ring #18.

† Parts included in Motor-Pump Assembly.

THE *NEW* GET RID OF BOAT ODORS

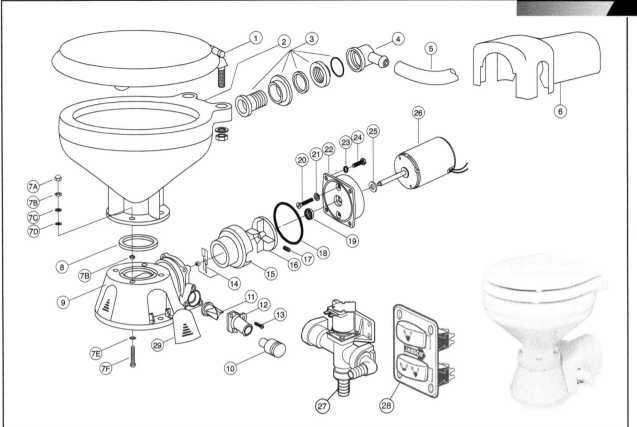

PARTS LIST

Key	Description	Qty. Req.	Part Number
1	Seat and Cover, Compact Size	1	29097-1000
	Seat and Cover, Regular Size	1	29127-1000
1A	Hinge Only, Compact Size	1	29098-1000
	Hinge Only, Regular Size	1	29098-2000
2	Bowl, Compact Size	1	29096-0000
	Bowl, Regular Size	1	29126-0000
3 & 4	Bowl Spud & Intake Elbow & O-ring	1	29048-0000
5	Hose, 6 feet	1	29035-1031
6	Motor Cover †	1	37042-1000
7	Bowl Installation Hardware	1	18753-0637
7A	Nut Cap**	4	
7B	Hex Nut** (Two places)	8	
7C	Washer, Stainless Steel**	4	
7D	Washer, Plastic**	4	
7E	Washer, Starlock**	4	
7F	Phillips Head Screw**	4	
8	Bowl O-Ring Seal	1	44101-1000
9	Base Assembly**	1	37004-1000
10	1-1/2" Adapter, Discharge Port	1	98023-0080
11	Joker Valve* **	1	44106-1000
12	1" Discharge Port**	1	44107-1000
13	Screw**	3	96050-0568
14	Chopper Plate with Lock Nut †	1	37056-1000
15	Macerator Housing †	1	37014-0000
16	Centrifugal Impeller †	1	37006-0000

Key	Description	Qty. Req.	Part Number
17	Set Screw †	1	91084-0320
18	O-ring* †	1	43990-0066
19	Seal* †	1	1040-0000
20	Screw †	2	91010-0144
21	Washer, Plastic* †	2	35445-0000
22	Seal Housing † 1	1	37043-1000
23	Lock Washer #10, Stainless Steel †	4	
24	Screw †	4	91027-0011
25	Slinger †	1	6342-0000
26	Motors:		
	Motor - 12 Volt †	1	18753-0554
	Motor - 24 Volt †	1	18753-0555
27	Solenoid Valve & Siphon 12 Volt	1	37038-1012
	Solenoid Valve & Siphon	1	
	Breaker 24 Volt	1	37038-1024
28	Switch Panel	1	37047-2000
29	Screw Covers (3/kit)	1	37003-1000
	Service Kit		90197-0000
	Motor & Pump Assembly		
	12 Volt EMC		37072-0092
	24 Volt EMC		37072-0094

* Parts Supplied with Service Kit.
** Parts included with base 37004-1000.
† Parts included in Motor & Pump Assembly.

Part No.	Description
1108A	Macerator Nut
1222AW	90° Discharge Fitting
1226	Mounting Screw (4)
1226B	1/4-20 Hex Nut (4)
1234	Bowl Gasket
1236AW	Bowl Spud Assembly
1236E	Bowl Elbow
1237	Marine-size Bowl
1244	Household-style Bowl
1610*	Motor
161105	Base
161107	Seal Plate O-Ring
161110	Seal Plate
161115	Impeller
161120	Impeller/Macerator Housing
161123	Macerator Blade
161125	Discharge Mounting Flange
161130	Discharge Fitting
162135	Cone Seal
162225	O-Ring
162305	Lower Housing includes #162315
162310	Diaphragm includes #162315
162315	Piston (4)
162320	Piston Seat (4) includes #162315
162325A	Bearing Plate Assembly includes #162315
162405	3/4" Hose Barb - 90° Fitting
162410	3/4" Hose Barb - Straight Fitting (2)
162415	Plug Fitting
162420	Fitting Clip (3)
162425	Fitting O-Ring (4)
161140	Motor Cover

Part No.	Description
162100W	Upper Housing Assembly
162200W	Middle Housing Assembly
162300W	Lower Housing Assembly
163000	Inline Strainer
164000	Push Button Switch
31-102	Shaft Seal
41-260	Bowl Elbow (Freshwater Models Only)
C254	Joker Valve
CH38	1/4-20 Threaded Stud (4)
F005	Set Screw
F020	Piston Fastener (4)
F144	Mounting Bolt Washer (4)
F162VT	Mounting Bolt
F164	Discharge Mounting Flange Fastener(4)
HW1	Mounting Screw Lockwasher (4)
M23A	Macerator Lockwasher (5)

Repair Kits

DIAPUMPRK	Diaphragm Pump Repair Kit
SEADISRK	SeaEra Discharge Repair Kit

* Specify DC Voltage (12, 24, 32)

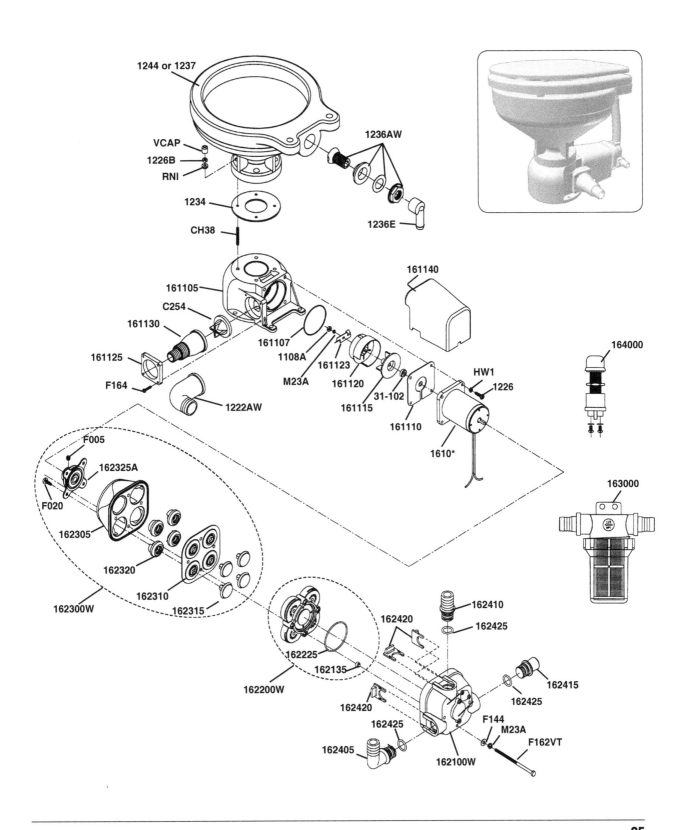

ItemNo.	Part No.	Description
1	1245	Seat & Cover
1	1245A	Seat & Cover (Almond)
2	221100	ME Bowl, Std Hgt, Angled Back, White
2	221100A	ME Bowl, Std Hgt, Angled Back, Almond
2	221101	ME Bowl, Std Hgt, Straight Back, White
2	AL002AW	ME Bowl, Std Hgt, Straight Back, Almond
2	231100	ME Bowl, Tall, Angled Back, White
2	231100A	ME Bowl, Tall, Angled Back, Almond
2	231101	ME Bowl, Tall, Straight Back, White
2	231101A	ME Bowl, Tall, Straight Back, Almond
3	M23A	#10 Lockwasher SS (5)
4	1108A	10-32 SS Nut
5	161123	Macerator Blade
6	31-102	Motor Shaft Seal
7	221110	Discharge Pump Seal Plate
8	221105	O-Ring
9	161115	Impeller
10	221115	Discharge Pump Macerator Housing
11	31-114	Lock Nut 10-32 W/Nylon(3)
12	221012	Discharge Motor 12 V
12	221024	Discharge Motor 24V
13	221125	Bowl Throat Adapter Clamp - Pump
14	221120	Bowl Throat Adapter
15	221130	Bowl Throat Adapter Clamp - Bowl
16	221155	Pump Mtg. Bracket, Angled Back Bowl
16	221156	Pump Mtg Bracket, Striaght Back Bowl
17	F193VT	Screw 10-32 X 3/8 W/VT
21	221140	Discharge Hose
22	221135	Joker Valve (2)
23	221145	Discharge Adapter Fitting
24	221146	Joker Valve Insert
25	221160	Discharge Hose Clamp (small)
26	221165	Discharge Hose Clamp (large)
27	VLVE	Vent Valve Assembly
28	FC001	Vent Valve Hose Clamp
29	221150	Spud Seal
31	221210	ME Bowl Mtg Bushing (2)
31	221210A	ME Bowl Mtg Bushing Almond (2)
32	F186VT	Screw Bowl Mtg (2)
33	221215	ME Bowl Mtg Cap (2)
33	221215A	ME Bowl Mtg Cap Almond
34	F196	ME Front Mounting Cap
34	F196A	ME Front Mounting Cap Almond
35	F187VT	Screw ME Bowl Mtg
36	F195	Washer Cup
37	F199	Bushing Bowl Mtg
38	221240A	Cam Nut (2)
39	F197	Cage Nut

REMOTE INTAKE PUMP UNITS

40	166012	Pump Motor 12VDC
40	166024	Pump Motor 24VDC
41	162000W	Remote Intake Pump w/o Motor
42	162405	3/4" Hose Barb 90° Fitting
43	162410	3/4" Hose Barb Straight
44	162415	Plug Fitting
45	162420	Fitting Retaining Clip (3)
46	162425	O-ring (3)
47	F162VT	Inlet Pump Mounting Bolt (4)
48	F144	#10 Washer SS Flat (4)
50	PLA26	Elbow Adapter 3/4 X 1/2

PRESSURIZED FRESH WATER UNITS

71	221300	Vacuum Breaker Assembly
72	221351	Solenoid Valve 12VDC
72	221352	Solenoid Valve 24VDC
73	221335	Hose 1/2"
74	221340	Hose Clamps 1/2" (2)
75	221356	ME Nut 3/4 BSP
75	221357	ME Hose Adadpter Straight

PARTS NOT SHOWN

	221175	L Bolt (2)
	F321	Washer Fender Style (3)
	F188	Well Nut 10-32 (3)
	F144	Washer #10L 18-8 SS (2)

FLUSH CONTROL OPTIONS
SMART TOILET CONTROL

	STC	Smart Toilet Control (12 & 24 VDC)
80	STC548	Smart Toilet Control (12 & 24 VDC)
81	STC545	Control Cable 7 ft
82	221524	Wall Switch Cover Plate White
82	221524A	Wall Switch Cover Plate Almond
83	STC543	Touch Panel w/Back Plate
84	221525	Touch Panel Gasket

MULTIFUNCTION MOMENTARY CONTROL (NOT SHOWN)

	221553	Manual (Relay) Control
	W183C	Cable for Multifunction Control
	SF71	Frame, Vimar
	SF74	Bazel , Vimar white
	SF77	Switch, Vimar

PUSH BUTTON SWITCH

	164000BR	Heavy Duty Switch, Brass

MOUNTING BRACKET ASSEMBLY

90	221230W	Mounting Bracket w/Hardware (includes items 31-39, 91 and 92)
91	221205	Bowl Mtg Bracket (3)
92	221230	Mounting Bracket Base

REPAIR KITS

	MERK	Discharge Pump Repair Kit

ADDITIONAL ACCESSORIES AVAILABLE FROM RARITAN

1PCP22	C.P. Cleans Potties, 22 OZ
1PCHGAL	Cleans Hoses, Tanks and MSD (gal)
SFH	Sanitation Hose 1 1/2" (sold by foot)
163000	Seawater Inline Strainer
TD90319	Vented Loop 3/4" (19mm) White
TD90321	Vented Loop 1" (25mm) White
TD90323	Vented Loop 1 1/2" (38mm) White
TD90314W	Aquavalve White w/ 3 TD90294 Tails
RTME12D	Power Converter for 120/240 VAC
ADS	Deodorant System (Seawater Models)

STCTSA: Holding Tank Full Sensor (Sensa Level TM) For use with STC Flush Control.

STCFL: Holding Tank Full Sensor (Float Switch) For use with STC Flush Control.

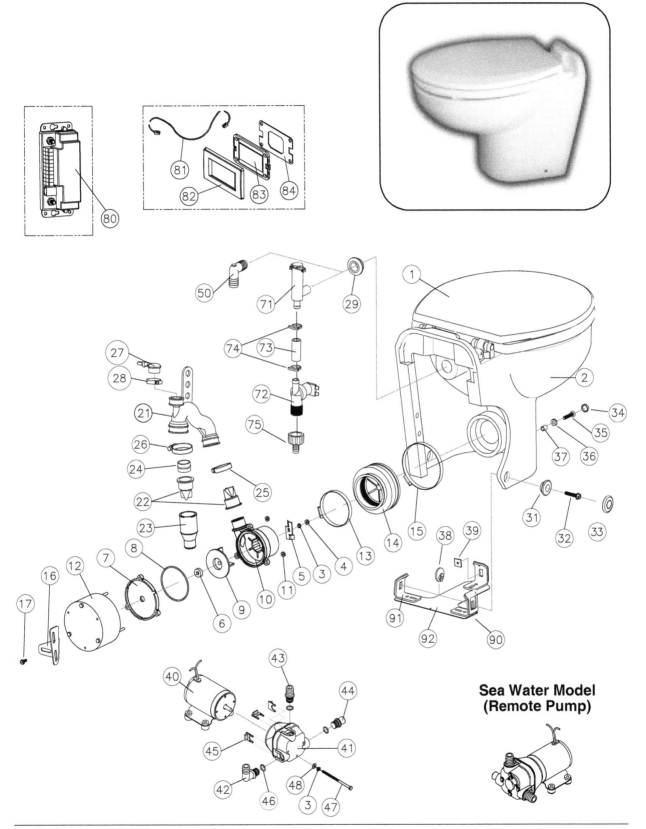

**Sea Water Model
(Remote Pump)**

PART #	DESCRIPTION
1118(4)	1/4" Locking Star Washer
1119(2)	1/4-20 x 3/4" Hex screw
1222AW	90° Discharge w/Flange
1222B	Straight Discharge
1226B(2)	1/4-20 Nut S/S
1236AW	Spud Assembly
1236E	Bowl Elbow
162100W	Upper Housing Assembly
162135(4)	Cone Seal
162200W	Middle Housing Assembly
162225	O-Ring
162300W	Lower Housing Assembly
162305	Lower Housing
162310	Diaphragm
162315	Piston (4)
162320	Piston Seat (4)
162325A	Bearing Plate Assembly
162405	3/4" Hose Barb 90° Fitting
162410	3/4" Hose Barb Straight
162415	Plug Fitting
162420 (3)	Fitting Clip
162425	O-Ring
1660*A	Pump Motor
31-102	Motor Shaft Seal
41-260	Bowl Elbow (Freshwater Units not shown)
AM001+	Atlantes Bowl (white)
AL001+	Atlantes Elongated Bowl (white)
AM020B	Pump Mounting Bracket
AM028	Bushing
AM030+	Atlantes Seat & Cover (white)
AM031	Discharge Connection (3 pieces)
AM101*B	Motor
AM110	Discharge Pump Back
AM114	Discharge Pump "O" Ring
AM130A	Discharge Pump Body
AM140	Discharge Cover
AM141	Discharge Cover O-Ring
AM161	Grinder Impeller
AM162	Grinder Teeth
AM165	Terminal Block Bracket
AM203	Remote Inlet Pump Base (not shown)
AM515	Atlantes Pump Mounting Bracket
AM519	Intake Hose from diaphragm pump
C254	Joker Valve
CH42 (2)	3/4" Reinforced Hose
CH43(5)	Hose Clamp S/S
ETB3	Terminal Block
F005(2)	1/4-20 x 5/16 SS Hex SOC
F030	1/4-20 x 2" Rnd. Hd. Screw S/S
F035(3)	Isolation Nut
F069	1/4" Fiber Washer
F071	Nylon Shoulder Washer (not shown)
F089(2)	1/4-20 x 1 3/4" Rnd. Hd. Screw S/S
F104	Panel Nut Brass Hex 5/8-32 x 7/8 x 1/8
F105NP(2)	1/4-28 set screw with nylon patch
F106	Plastite screw #6 x 3/4
F108	Screw #4 x 1
F111(4)	10-32 S/S Nut
F112(2)	8-32 x 1/4" Screw
F142VT(8)	10-32 x 5/8" Pan Hd. S/S Screw (not shown)
F143VT(2)	10-32 x 1" Pan Hd. SLTD S/S Screw
F144(2)	#10 S/S Flat Washer
F145VT(1)	10-32 x 1 3/4" Pan Hd. SLTD S/S Screw
F146VT(2)	1/4-20 x 1 1/4" Rnd. Hd. Screw S/S W/VT
F147VT(2)	3/8-16 x 1 1/2" Rnd. Hd. Screw S/S
F148VT(8)	8-32 x 7/16" S/S Truss Hd. Screw
F162VT	Mounting Bolt
HLWQB(4)	1/4" Split Lock Washer
HSB1(2)	1/4-20 Brass Screw
M23A(19)	#10 Lockwasher S/S
M30(4)	1/4-20 Brass Nut
M31(8)	1/4" Brass Flat Washer
RNI	Nylon Shoulder Washer
RTAH24D	Transformer/Rectifier for 120/240 VAC (not shown)

WALL MOUNTED FLUSH CONTROL

1226A	1/4-20 X 1 1/4" Rnd. Hd. Screw S/S
31-608	Cable for Flush Control (14 ft.)
AM028	Bushing
ATW*	Flush Control PCB Assy.
ATW640	Flush Control with Bezel Back Plate (White)
ATW640A	Flush Control with Bezel Back Plate (Bone)
ATW640B	Flush Control with Bezel Back Plate (Black)
F153	#4 1/2 Oval slotted
F170	6/32 - 7/8" screw

SOLENOID VALVE

CWPS*A	1/2" GC Solenoid Valve
CWPSMB	Mounting Bracket for CWPS*
PLA14 (2)	1/2" MPT to 3/4" Barbed Nipple

ATMOSPHERIC (ANTI-SIPHON) VACUUM BREAKER

PLA5	1/2" MPT PVC Nipple
PLA6	1/2" FPT to 3/4" Barbed Elbow
PLA7	1/2" MPT to 3/4" Barbed Nipple
PLAVB0-5	Atmospheric (anti-siphon) Vacuum Breaker

T-CHECK VALVE PARTS LIST

31-307D	Valve Body
31-307D1	Outlet Adapter
31-307E	"O" Ring
31-307W	T-Check Valve Assembly Complete
31-308W	Siphon Check Valve
CH8	Check Valve Spring
CH12	Check Ball

DEODORANT/SALT FEED PARTS LIST (ADS)

31-301	Salt Feed Tank
31-302	Salt Feed Tank Cap
31-304C	Plastic Tubing Clamp
31-304F	Bulkhead Fitting
31-304G	Bulkhead Fitting Nut
31-304H	Bulkhead Fitting Seal
31-304W	Assembly (includes part #'s 31-304C, 31-304F, 31-304G, 31-304H, 31-305)
31-305	PVC Clear Tubing 1/4"

ADDITIONAL ACCESSORIES AVAILABLE FROM RARITAN

1PCP22	C.P., Cleans Potties, Bio-enzymatic, 22 oz.
AHDA1W	Internal Vented Loop
CON22	Raritan Concentrate 22 oz. bottle
SH	Sanitation Hose (sold by the foot)
VL 1 1/2	Vented Loop 1 1/2"
VL 3/4	Vented Loop 3/4"
YV	"Y" Valve

§Parts are NOT included with Wall Switch Flush Control Models
+CHOICE OF COLOR
*SPECIFY VOLTAGE

ELECTRIC TOILET ATLANTES FREEDOM
EXPLODED VIEW

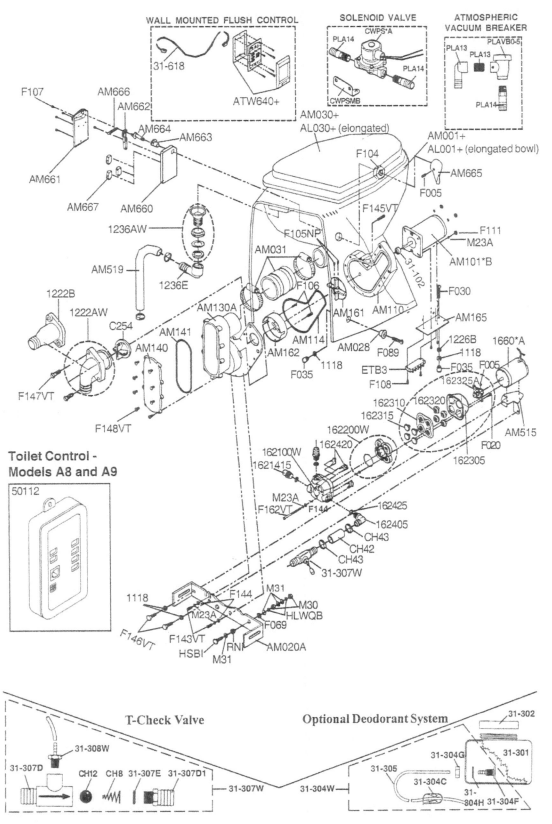

(Quantities are one unless otherwise indicated)

Before ordering, locate required part on exploded parts view to be sure you are ordering the correct part for your CROWN HEAD.

Part No.	Description
1118	Lockwasher (4)
1203B1	"O" Ring
1222AW	Discharge Ell and Flange
1222B	Straight Discharge
1222BW	Straight Discharge Assembly (Incl. 1222B, CH90, CH92, [2]1115, C253, [4]CH27)
1226B	Bowl Mounting Nut (4)
1341	Discharge Screw (2)
31-102	Motor Shaft Seal
C253	Joker Valve
CH102MW	Intake Pump Assembly, complete
CH119MW	Discharge Impeller Assy. (Incl. CH119M, [2]F149VT)
CH12	Check Ball
CH120	Discharge Pump Wall
CH121	Macerator
CH136	Siphon Cap for Shroud Bottle
CH15DD	End Bell
CH18W	Front Cover (w/"O" ring)
CH2	Pump Body (w/shaft seal)
CH25	Front Cover "O" Ring
CH26	Front Cover Screw (6)
CH27	Mounting Screw (4)
CH291	Shroud (2 pcs.)
CH291ALM	Shroud, Bone (2 pcs.)
CH29A	Shroud Bottle (Concentrate Reservoir)
CH29B	Shroud Screw (2)
CH29A1W	Shroud Assembly, Complete w/bottle, cap and siphon
CH336W	Siphon Assembly, Complete (Incl. CH136, CH37, CH37E)
CH34	Woodruff Key
CH37	Siphon Tubing
CH37E	Siphon Check Valve
CH38	Bowl Stud (4)
CH42	Hose
CH43P	Hose Clamp (2)
CH5VW	Pump Plug, Vented(Incl. 1203B1 O Ring)
CH50CW	Bowl Elbow w/Siphon Intake
CH51	Base Screw (4)
CH52	Rubber Mounting Strip (2) not shown
CH53	Pump Mounting Screw (4)
CH55A	Base Plate
CH57	Slinger
CH58	End Bell Screw (4)
CH59	Seal with Stainless Steel Spring
CH6	Pump Cover Plate
CH7	Pump Gasket
CH8	Check Valve Spring
CH90	Discharge Adapter
CH92	Adapter Gasket
CHM*	Motor

Part No.	Description
F149VT	Set Screw (2)
G13	Pump Impeller
G15	Impeller Washer (2)
G13W	Pump Impeller w/(2) G15
G2M	Impeller Wear Plate
M23	Lockwasher (4)
M30	Hex Nut, Brass (2)
M31	Flat Washer, Brass (2)
RNI	Nylon Bowl Mounting Washer (4)
VCAP	Vinyl Cap (bowl nut cover)

MISCELLANEOUS RELATED PARTS

Part No.	Description
1234	Bowl Gasket (fits all Raritan toilets)
1236AW	Bowl Spud Assembly
1237W	Marine-size Bowl, Round Top Rim (white only), incl. 1236AW
1238A	Seat and Cover for Marine-size Bowl (white only)
1244W	Household-style Bowl, Oval Top Rim available in white or bone, includes 1236AW 1245 Seat and Cover for Household-style Bowl
163000	In-Line Strainer
1PCP22	C.P., Cleans Potties, Bio-enzymatic, 22 oz.
CDS*	Continuous Duty Solenoid Relay
CHTT9	Hose Clamp for 1 1/2" I.D. Hose
CON22	Raritan Concentrate 22 oz.
CSRK	Repair Kit (Centrifugal DischargeSeries) Includes: CH25, CH92, 1234, CH12, G13, CH8, CH37E, RNI, CH120, C253, CH59, 31-102, CH7, G15, 1203B1and CH57
CDPUMPRK	Crown Head CD Series & CHII Intake Pump Repair Kit (built before 4/95) Includes:1203B1, CH12, G13, G2M, 31-102, CH7 and G15
CDDISRK	Crown Head CD Series Discharge Repair Kit; Includes: 1234, CH120, CH57, CH92, C253, CH25 and CH59
CR1	Discharge Impeller and Macerator Assy. (incl. CH120, CH121, F149VT[2], and CH119MW)
PBS	Pushbutton Switch
RHT4	Inline Check Valve for 1 1/2" I.D. Hose RTC* Raritan Off-delay Timer
RTCH24DA	Rectified Transformer (for 120 or 240 VAC input)
SH	Sanitation Hose, 1 1/2" I.D. (sold by the foot)
SL	Super-Lube 1/2 oz. tube
VL 3/4	Vented Loop 3/4"
VL 1 1/2	Vented Loop 1 1/2"
YV	"Y" Valve for 1 1/2" I.D. Hose

*Specify Voltage

ELECTRIC TOILET CROWN HEAD CD
PARTS LIST

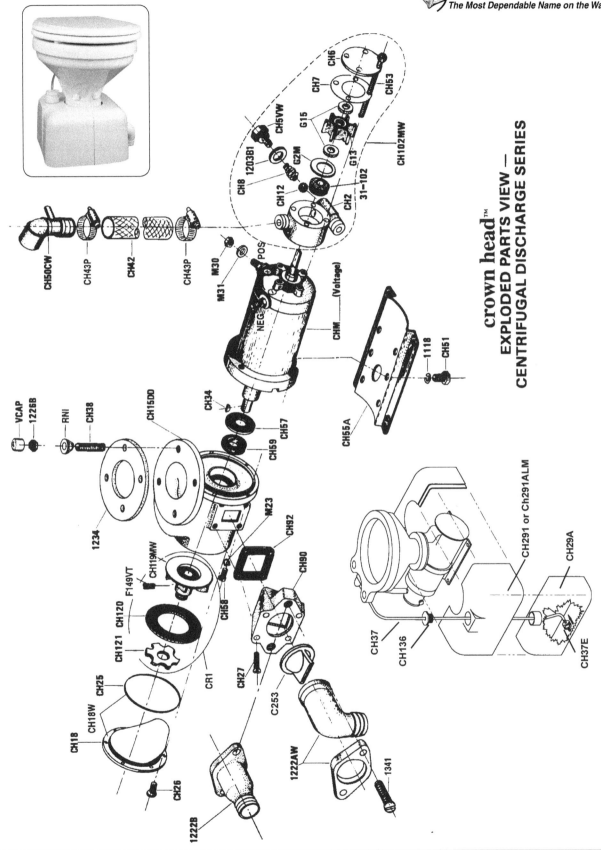

crown head™
EXPLODED PARTS VIEW —
CENTRIFUGAL DISCHARGE SERIES

TECMA

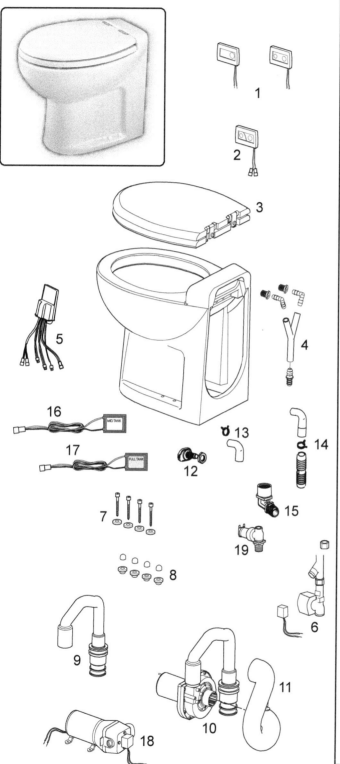

Key No.	Part No.	DESCRIPTION
1	36082	Control Panel – Single Switch; Analog
	38072	Control Panel – Double Switch; Analog
2	38645	Wall Switch w/Waterproof Connectors (select models w/Micro-P controller)
3	38176	Seat/Cover – White (Gold Hinges) (Plus models)
	36504	Seat/Cover – White (Chrome Hinges) (Plus models)
	36503	Seat/Cover – Bone (Chrome Hinges) (Plus models)
	38134	Seat/Cover – Bone (Gold Hinges) (Plus models)
	38133	Seat/Cover – Black (Gold Hinges) (Plus models)
	38132	Seat/Cover – Black (Chrome Hinges) (Plus models)
	38197	Seat & Cover – Bone (Chrome Hinges) (Std models)
	38194	Seat & Cover – White (Chrome Hinges) (Std models)
4	38200	Flush Water Inlet Service Kit
5	38646	Controller w/Waterproof Connectors (select models)
6	38141	CEME Solenoid Valve – Marine 12V
	38142	CEME Solenoid Valve – Marine 24V
7	38066	Hex Head Closet Bolts – White (4)(Plus)
	38067	Hex Head Closet Bolts – Bone (4)(Plus)
	38260	Hex Head Closet Bolts – Black (4)(Plus)
8	36508	Cap and Bushings – White
	38139	Cap and Bushings – Gold
	36509	Cap and Bushings – Chrome
9	38061	Discharge Pipe (1.5" Connection)
10	38056	Pump/Motor with Discharge Pipe – 12V
	38058	Pump/Motor with Discharge Pipe – 24V
11	38190	Discharge Hose Service Kit
12	36746	Nozzle Kit – White
	36747	Nozzle Kit – Bone
13	38651	Short Inlet Tube Kit
14	38657	Short Inlet Tube & Hose Barb Tool (pump version)
15	38652	Reducer/Adaptor Kit
16	36818	Mid-Tank Sensor w/Waterproof Connectors (select models w/Micro-P controller)
17	36790	Full-Tank Sensor w/Waterproof Connectors (select model w/Micro-P controller)
18	38148	Marine Water Pump – 12V
	38147	Marine Water Pump – 24V
19	38064	Invensys Solenoid – 12V (select models w/Micro-P controller)
	38650	Invensys Solenoid – 24V (select models w/Micro-P controller)

SELF-PRIMING MACERATOR PUMP WITH RUN-DRY PROTECTION

FEATURES

Pump: Self-Priming Flexible Impeller with Stainless Steel Wearplate

Impeller: Jabsco Nitrile compound

EXPLODED VIEW

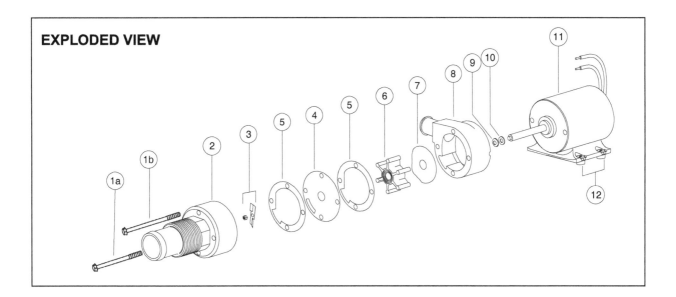

PARTS

Key	Describtion	Qty.	Part No.
1a	Bolt Short	2	See bolt kit
1b	Bolt Long	2	See bolt kit
2	Macerator Housing	1	18594-1000
3	Chopper Plate with Locknut	1	37056-2000
4	Wearplate, Large	1	18597-1000
5	Gaskets (2 each per kit)*	1	18596-1000
6	Impeller*	1	6303-0003
7	Wearplate, Small	1	12316-1002
8	Body*	1	18593-1000
9	Seal*	1	1040-0000
10	Slinger	1	6342-0000
11	Motor 12 Volt	1	17246-1012
	Motor 24 Volt	1	17246-1024
12	Grommets (Set of 4)	1	92900-0120
	Service Kit	1	18598-1000
	Bolt Kit	1	17288-1000

*These parts are supplied in 18598-1000 Service Kit.

Part Numbers		
Model	**Voltage**	**Fuse Sizes**
50890-1000	12V	10A
50890-1100	24V	5A
Service Kit (Includes*)		
SK890	Service Kit - Waste Pump	

Key	Description	*Quantity in Kit
1	Bracket	
2	Bush	
3	Clamp Bottom	
4	Clamp Top	
5	Con Rod	
6	Con Rod Plate	
7	Cover	1
8	Diaphragm	1
9	Hex Head Screw	
10	Hex Head Screw	4
11	Motor Assembly	
12	Screw Recessed Pan Head	1
13	Socket Head Screw	
14	Washer	1
15	Waste Pump Chamber	
16	Waste Pump Joker Valve	2
17	Waste Pump Port	2
18	Washer	

THE *NEW* GET RID OF BOAT ODORS

Macerator Pump 53100

Macerator pump 53101 with Waste Valve

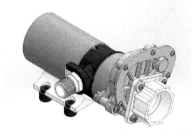

Smart Macerator control (optional)

Repair Kits:

53100R K: Include s 4,5,7,12
53101R K: Include s 4,5,7,12,21,33,35,38

Part List

No.	Part#	Description
1	53105	**Motor**
3	53110W	Pump Housing (includes 4,12)
4	31-102	Shaft Seal
5	53120W	Impeller (includes 2, 7)
6	53130	Wear Plate, SS
7	53135	Gasket
8	53140	Pump Cover, SS
9	53145	Macerator Blade, SS
10	53166	Discharge Adapter 3/4 - 14 MNPT
11	53168	Discharge Adapter 1" Insert
12	53169	O-ring, Discharge Adapter Nipple
13	53167	Discharge Adapter Retaining Clip
14	53160	10-32 x 3" Stud
15	M23A	#10 Lock Washer, SS
16	1108A	10-32 Nut SS
17	53155	Teeth Housing
18	F144	#10 18-8 SS Flat Washer

**Specify Voltage 12 or 24*

No.	Part#	Description
19	53156	Teeth Housing
20	53165	Pump Adapter
21	25103	Pump Adapter O Ring
22	F326	1/4-20 x 1 3/4" Hex CAP Head Screws
23	1226B	1/4 " SS Nut
24	53180	WVA Adapter 1 1/2" FNPT
26	53181	10-32 x 1/2" Adapter Screws
27	53183	10-24 Nut SS
28	53182	10-24 x 1 3/4" Adapter Screw
29	31-121	1 1/2" Male Adapter
WASTE VALVE ASSEMBLY (WVA)		
30	53170	1 1/2" WVA Assy.
31	53171	WVA Housing
32	53174	WVA Cover
33	53176	WVA Housing O-ring
34	53172	WVA Valve Gate
35	53179	WVA Adapter Seals
36	F403	8-16 x 1/2" Screw
37	53175	WVA Shaft
38	53173	WVA Shaft O-ring

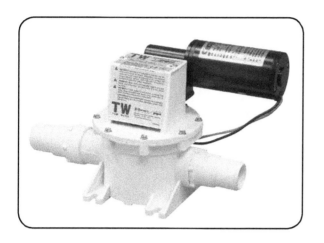

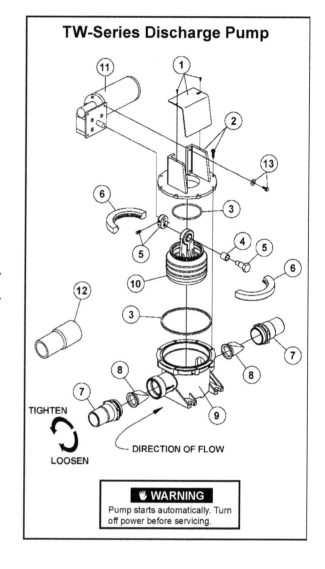

TW-Series Discharge Pump

TIGHTEN

LOOSEN

DIRECTION OF FLOW

⚠ WARNING
Pump starts automatically. Turn
off power before servicing.

Item	Part No.	Description
1	385311422	Pump Cover Kit
2	385311225	Pump Top Closure Kit
3	385310151	O-Ring Replacement Kit
4	385310242	Bellows Bushing
5	385310644	Eccentric Kit
6	385311226	Bellows Clamp Kit
7	385311843	Valve Nipple
8	385310076	1.5" Duckbill Valve
9	385311858	Pump Body
10	385230980	Bellows Assembly (includes item 4)
11	385311065	12 VDC Motor (includes item 5)
	385311066	24 VDC Motor (includes item 5)
12	307341113	1" x 1.5" Reducing Adapter (optional)
13	385311224	Mounting Hardware Kit
		Not Shown
	385310250	Pump Assembly Less Motor (includes items 1-9)

*Note: When reassembling pump, tighten screws (included with Item 2) to 20±2lbs., or until snug. Over-tightening will cause holes to strip.

THE *NEW* GET RID OF BOAT ODORS

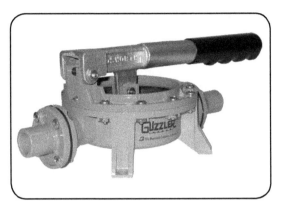

ITEM	PART NAME		
1	INLET FLANGE		
2	OUTLET FLANGE		
3	BUTTON		
4	CLEVIS		
5	BODY		
6	CLAMP RING		
7			
9	HORIZONTAL HANDLE W/ ACTUATOR		
9A	VERTICAL HANDLE W/GRIP		
10			
11A	VERTICAL ACTUATOR		
12	HARDWARE SET		
	PPH10-24X5/8	(8)	INLET/OUTLET
	PPH10-24X3/4	(10)	CLAMP RING
	PPH10-24X1/2	(2)	CLAMP RING
	HN10-24	(18)	
	TH10-24	(18)	
	TH1/4-20X1/2	(1)	DIAPHRAGM
13	DIAPHRAGM		
14	FLAPPER VALVES		
PS4-5	PIN SET		

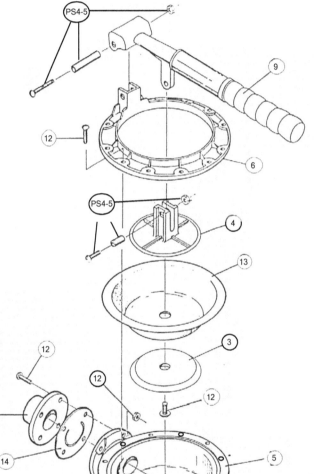

RARITAN
The Most Dependable Name on the Water

TREATMENT UNIT

Part No.	Description
32-102AW	Mixer Motor 2 1/2" Dia. 12 VDC
33-102AW	Mixer Motor 2 1/2" Dia. 24 VDC
34-102AW	Mixer Motor 2 1/2" Dia. 32 VDC

NOTE: All motors include 31-102, Seal washer, Retaining ring and 31-103.

Part No.	Description
31-121	Hose Fitting (2)
31-120	Discharge Elbow 90°
M30	Electrode Nut 1/4-20 Brass (4)
M31	Electrode #14 Brass flat washer (4)
31-103	Motor Shaft Bushing (2)
31-106	10-32x7/8"RHMS,S/S (4)
31-109	Mixer Impeller
31-110-1	Impeller Bolt, 12-24x5/8", S/S (2)
31-110-2	Impeller Lock Washer, #12, S/S (2)
31-113-2	Terminal Block Bolt (2)
31-134	Cover Hold Down Screw 10-32 x 1 Hex(16)
31-114	Cover Hold Down Nut, 10-32 (18)
31-115	Treatment Tank
31-122	Intake Plug
32-5000	Electrode Pack 12 VDC
33-5000	Electrode Pack 24 VDC
34-5000	Electrode Pack 32 VDC
31-112	Cover Gasket
31-108	Macerator Set Screw, 8-32x3/16", S/S
31-107	Macerator Impeller
31-101W	Treatment Cover
31-104CW	Crossover Plug
31-105	O-Ring
31-102	Motor Shaft Seal (2)
31-102-1	Macerator Seal Washer
31-102-2	Macerator Retaining Ring
31-102-3	Mixer Seal Washer
31-102-4	Mixer Retaining Ring
32-101AW	Macerator Motor 3" Dia. 12 VDC
33-101AW	Macerator Motor 3" Dia. 24 VDC
34-101AW	Macerator Motor 3" Dia. 32 VDC
ETB2	Terminal Block

Part No.	Description
31-3001	Salt tank unit complete, two gallon (not shown)
31-3005	Four gallon salt feed tank (not shown)
32-3005	Four gallon salt feed tank w/12 volt pump (not shown)
33-3005	Four gallon salt feed tank w/24 volt pump (not shown)
32-7000	12 V DC Treatment Unit - No Control Unit, System Status Panel or LCD Display
33-7000	24 V DC Treatment Unit - No Control Unit, System Status Panel or LCD Display
34-7000	32 V DC Treatment Unit - No Control Unit, System Status Panel or LCD Display

CONTROL

Part No.	Description
31-618	Cable for LCD and System Status Panel (not shown) 16'
31-702	LCD Display
31-705	System Status Panel
32-700	Control Unit 12V
33-700	Control Unit 24V
34-700	Control Unit 32V
WAES01T	Wire Harness (not shown)

PARTS BAG (packed with each new unit)

Part No.	Description
31-111	Cable Clamp 1/2 x 1/2
31-717	Insulating Bushing (4)
ETP1	Terminal Protector Red
F110	Screw 6 x 1/2 Phil Pad HD (4) to mount Display and Start/Stop button

ESTRK (EST Repair Kit)

Part No.	Description
31-102	Motor Shaft Seal (2)
31-102-1	Macerator Seal Washer
31-102-2	Macerator Retaining Ring
31-102-3	Mixer Seal Washer
31-102-4	Mixer Retaining Ring
31-103	Motor Shaft Bushing (2)
31-105	O-Ring
F351	10-32x7/8" w/ O-ring (4)
31-112	Cover Gasket
31-113-2	Terminal Block Bolt (4)
31-114	Cover Hold Down Nut, 10-32 (4)
SL1CC	Super Lube

NOTE: We recommend 3M 4000 UV to seal the motor hold down bolts (part# F351)

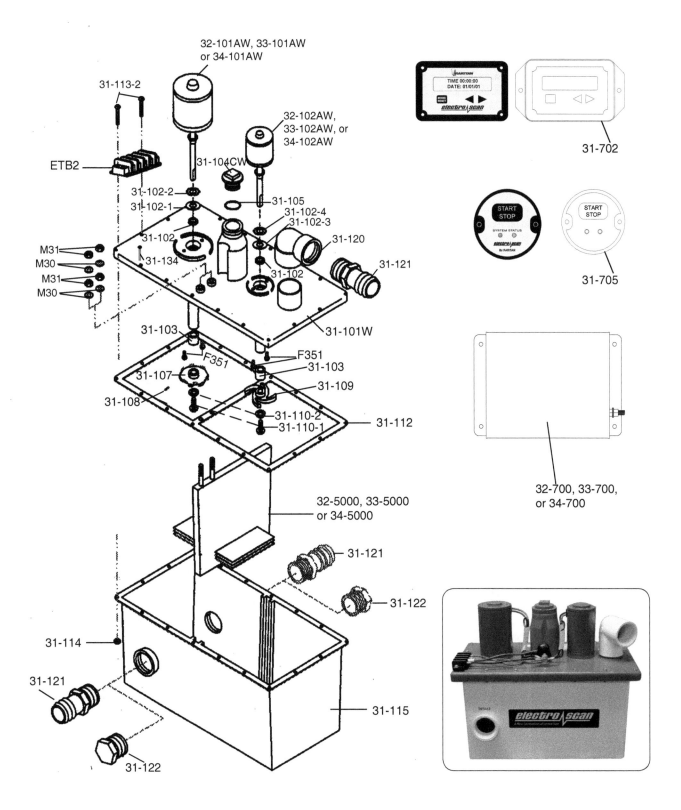

Item	Part No.	Description
1	32-102A**	Mixer Motor 2 1/2" Dia. 12 VDC
1	33-102A**	Mixer Motor 2 1/2" Dia. 24 VDC
1	34-102A**	Mixer Motor 2 1/2" Dia. 32 VDC
2	31-121	Hose Fitting (2)
3	31-120	Discharge Elbow 90°
4	M30	Electrode Flat Washer, 1/4", Brass (4)
5	M31	Electrode Lug Nut, 1/4"-20 Brass (4)
7	31-103	Motor Shaft Bushing (2)
8	31-106	10-32x7/8"RHMS,S/S (22) (Motor hold-down bolts must be completely covered with silicone caulk before final reassembly to prevent leaking.)
9	31-109	Mixer Impeller
10	31-110-1	Impeller Bolt, 12-24x5/8", S/S (2)
11	31-110-2	Impeller Lock Washer, #12, S/S (2)
12	31-114	Cover Hold Down Nut, 10-32 (18)
13	31-115	Treatment Tank
14	31-122	Intake Plug
15	32-5000	Electrode Pack 12 VDC
15	33-5000	Electrode Pack 24 VDC
15	34-5000	Electrode Pack 32 VDC
16	31-112	Cover Gasket
17	31-108	Macerator Set Screw, 8-32x3/16", S/S
18	31-107	Macerator Impeller
19	31-101W	Treatment Cover (Inc. 7, 20,21 and 22)
20	31-104C	Crossover Plug
21	31-105	O-Ring
22	31-102	Motor Shaft Seal (2)
23	32-101AW**	Macerator Motor 3" Dia. 12 VDC
23	33-101AW**	Macerator Motor 3" Dia. 24 VDC
23	34-101AW**	Macerator Motor 3" Dia. 32 VDC
	31-3001	Salt tank unit complete, two gallon (not shown)
	31-3002	Four gallon salt feed tank (not shown)
	32-3003	Four gallon salt feed tank w/12 volt pump (not shown)
	33-3003	Four gallon salt feed tankw/24 volt pump (not shown)
	32-4000*	12 V DC Complete Treatment Unit (Items 1-22)
	33-4000*	24 V DC Complete Treatment Unit (Items 1-22)
	34-4000*	32 V DC Complete Treatment Unit (Items 1-22)

* Less Control Module

**NOTE: When replacing existing or new motor(s), clean area around motor mounting bolts with PVC cleaner before applying silicone caulk to motor hold down bolt heads (see Item #8). Dispense enough sealant to cover an area three times greater than the bolt heads to avoid leakage through bolt holes.

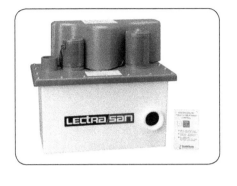

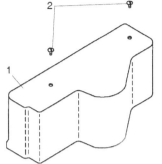

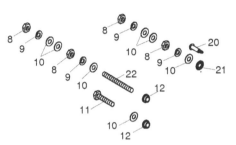

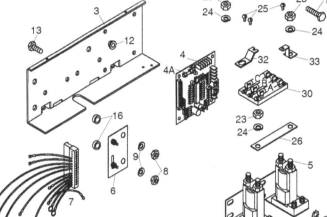

Item	Part No.	Description
1	31-460	Control Cover
2	CH26	8-32 x 7/16" Truss head screw (2)
3	31-462	Mounting Plate
4	32-601	Circuit Board, 12V
	33-601	Circuit Board, 24V
	34-601	Circuit Board, 32V
4A	EF5FA	F1 - 5 Amp Fuse, fast acting
5	AM06012	Solenoid Relay (2) - 12V
	AM06024	Solenoid Relay (2) - 24V
	AM06032	Solenoid Relay (2) - 32V
6	RBS501	Shunt 50 mv 50 amp LST/MC
7	31-402A	Wiring Harness Assy.
8	M30	1/4 - 20 Brass Nut (8)
9	HLWQB	1/4" Lockwasher (6)
10	M31	#14 Brass Flat Washer (7)
11	HSB1	1/4 - 20 Brass Cap Screw (2)
12	RNI	Nylon Shoulder Washer (3)
13	1119A	1/4 - 20 x 1/2" S/S Hex Head Machine Screw (4)
14	1118	1/4" External Tooth Washer (5)
15	1226B	1/4 - 20 S/S Hex Head Nut (4)
16	31-476	Nylon Spacer Washer (2)
20	F31-480	Nylon Stand Offs: PCB Supports (4)
21	F069	Gray Fiber Flat Washer
22	F31-478	Threaded Rod 1/4 - 20 x 2" Brass

L270 0802vkm

Item	Part No.	Description
23		5/16 - 24 Nut (4)
24		5/16 Lockwasher (4)
25		#6-32 Screw
26	31-464	Bracket
30	31-232	Fuse Block
30A	32-218	MDL 6 1/4 Fuse (12V)
30B	32-219	MDL 35 Fuse (12V)
30C	32-220	MDL 30 Fuse (12V)
31	31-466	Bracket
32	31-469	Copper Bracket
	31-468	Bracket (not shown)
33	31-470	Cond. Bracket
	32-602	12V Assy. (incl. all above parts except 1 and 2)
	33-602	24V Assy. (incl. all above parts except 1 and 2)
	34-602	32V Assy (incl all above parts except 1 and 2)
	31 603	Control Indicator Panel (not shown)
	31-604	Control Indicator Panel Cable (not shown)
	31-605	Activator Assembly for Manual Toilets (not shown)
	31-606	Pressure Switch for the Activator (not shown)

( ) Indicates Total pieces required

PURASAN PARTS LIST

Item	Part #	Description
1	32-102AW	Mixer Motor 2 1/2" Dia. 12 V DC
1	33-102AW	Mixer Motor 2 1/2" Dia. 24 VDC
		(1) includes shaft seals and bushing for mixer motor)
2	31-121	Hose Fitting (2)
(Not shown)		90° hose fitting (PLA401)
3	31-120	Discharge Elbow 90°
6	31-134	Cover Hold down Bolt, 10-32 x 1" (16)
		(not shown)
7	31-103	Motor Shaft Bushing (2) (see 62)
8	31-106	Motor Hold down Bolt, 10-32x1", S/S (4)
9	31-109	Mixer Impeller
10	31-110-1	Impeller Bolt, 12-24 x 5/8", S/S (2)
11	31-110-2	Impeller Lock Washer, #12, S/S (2)
12	31-114	Cover Hold down Nut, 10-32 (18)
13	31-115PS	Treatment Tank
14	31-122	Intake Plug
15	41-102	Tank Divider
16	31-112	Cover Gasket
17	31-108	Macerator Set Screw
18	31-107	Macerator Impeller
19	41-101W	Treatment Cover (includes 62,56, 25,26)
22	33-101AW*	Macerator Motor for 12 V DC unit
22	34-101AW*	Macerator Motor for 24, 32 V DC
(22)		includes shaft seal and bushing for Macerator motor
25	31-104CW	Crossover Plug with O-ring
26	31-105	O-Ring
51	M31	#14 Brass Flat Washer (4)
52	M30	1/4"-20 Brass Nut (4)
56	31-325A	Adapter Tank Lid
57	221335	Hose
58	41-159	Check valve
59	31-304C	Hose clamp
62	ESTRK	EST/PST Repair Kit includes following
(Not Shown)		31-102 Motor Shaft Seal(2)
		31-102-1 Macerator Seal Washer
		31-102-2 Macerator Retaining Ring
		31-102-3 Mixer Seal Washer
		31-102-4 Mixer Retaining Ring
		31-103 Motor Shaft Bushing(2)
		31-105 O-Ring
		31-106 10-32x 7/8" Screws (4)
		31-112 Cover Gasket

DRAIN MANIFOLD ASSEMBLY(41-137W)

Item	Part #	Description
24	41-151A	Adapter 1/4" x 1/2" elbow with check valve
27	41-145	Pull Solenoid
28	41-137	Drain Manifold assy.(with check valve)
29	41-151B	Adapter 1/8" x 1/4" elbow with check valve
30	41-141	1/4" NPT x 1/2" barbed adapter
31	PLA3	1/4" Barbed x 1/4" NPT Adapter
32	41-139	Cap, manifold
33	41-138C	1/4" x 3/4" U cup seal
34	41-138	Plunger
35	41-138A	Washer for plunger
36	F204	6-32 x 3/8"" Flat head mach. screw(4)
37	LWS	Spring

Item	Part #	Description
38	F203	Washer 5/16" x 3/4"
39	1305D	Clevis pin
53	41-152	Base Plate
54	F202	6-32 x 1/4" Flat head mach. screw (2)

TABLET DISPENSER (41-100AW)

Item	Part #	Description
40	41-130A	Dispenser Body.
41	41-177	Adapter 1/2"NPT x 1/2" barb
42	41-176	Elbow 1/2"NPT x 1/4"barb
43	41-156W	Tablet holder assembly.
44	41-135A	Purasan Tablets (sold saparately)
45	41-179	Float extension pipe
46	41-178W	Float sensor
47	RWS5A	"O" Ring
48	41-131M	Dispenser Cap (machined)
85	41-505	Cable for Float sensor

WATER Valve (221351W, 12V - 221352W, 24V)

Item	Part #	Description
65	221356W	Inlet hose adapter
66	PX50W	Double Check Valve assembly
67	221351	Water Solenoid 12V
67	221352	Water Solenoid 24V
68	221335	1/2" Hose

AIR PUMP for tablet dispenser (162000WA)

Item	Part #	Description
70	166024A **	Motor
71	162000W	Intake Pump Assembly,air pump
72	162415A	Plug with barbed fitting
	DIAPUMPRK	Diaphragm Pump Repair Kit

CONTROLS

Item	Part #	Description
80	SPC	Purasan Control
81	41-500A	Wall Panel circuit board
82	221514	ME: wall panel cover,white
83	221525	ME; wall panel gasket
84	31-618	Cable for SPC wall panel
86	FUSE10	ATO fuse 10A

OTHER (Not shown)

Part #	Description
41-135A	Purasan Tablets (Refill)
42-1000A	Treatment Unit Complete 12V
43-1000A	Treatmnet Unit Complete 24V
PSTDCEX	Purasan Dual Control

*NOTE: 12VDC units are equipped with a 24VDC Macerator Motor, 24VDC units are equipped with a 32VDC Macerator Motor.

**NOTE: All models use a 24VDC Air Pump Motor

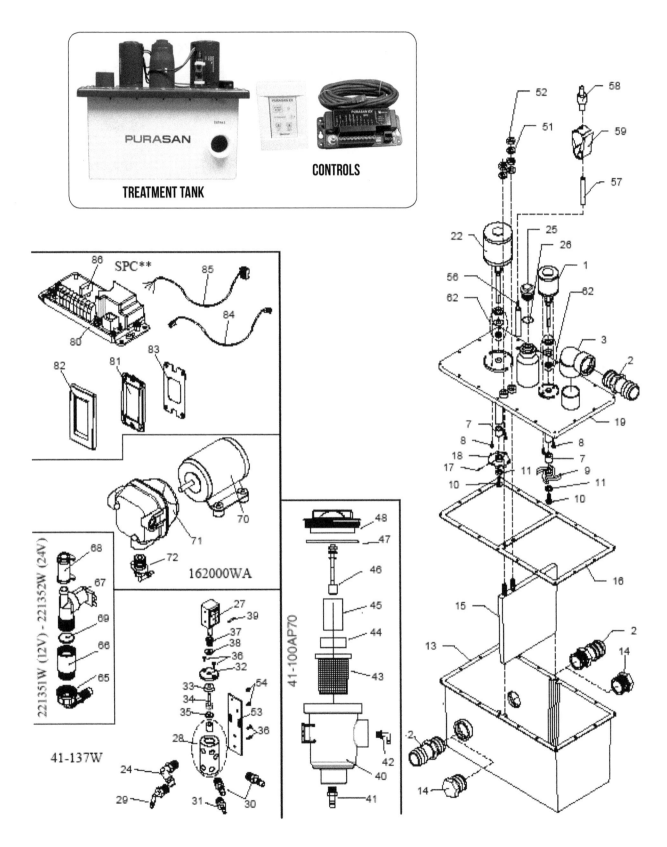

TREATMENT TANK

CONTROLS

SPC**

162000WA

41-137W

221351W (12V) - 221352W (24V)

41-100AP70

The Concept: Both aerobic and anaerobic bacteria exist naturally in raw sewage, but only the anaerobic cause unpleasant holding tank odors. Sweettank® upsets the balance between aerobic and anaerobic bacteria by inducing a continuous flow of air into the holding tank through a submerged bubbler. The process establishes an oxygen-rich environment in which anaerobic bacteria cannot survive. When the anaerobic bacteria are gone, so is the odor.

Before you Begin:

* Decide whether the installation will be into the top of the tank or through the side.

* Determine the holding tank depth at the chosen installation location.

* Confirm there is adequate unrestricted tank venting (5/8" ID minimum).

* Determine the location of the Sweettank® air pump. The pump makes an audible humming sound, so choose a location that is not adjacent to sleeping quarters, or on a hollow wall or bulkhead.

IMPORTANT INSTALLATION NOTE:

Several Push-to-Lock fittings are included. When assembling the bubbler, rigid tubes or air hose to the push-to-lock fittings, the component must be inserted FIRMLY into the push-to-lock fitting to assure proper air flow. Test the assembly in a glass of water to assure the bubbler produces a generous supply of bubbles BEFORE installing into the holding tank.

Tank-Top Installation (see Figure-1):

* The 1-1/2" PVC Plug Assembly screws hand-tight into a 1-1/2" NPT threaded opening. A threaded adaptor and rubber tank seal (fits into a 2-1/2" hole cut with a hole saw) are provided if you do not have a threaded opening available.

* Measure tank depth

* Assemble bubbler assembly to rigid tubes and sleeves, and then cut to suit tank depth.

Tank-Side Installation (see Figure-2):

* The 1-1/2" PVC Plug Assembly screws hand-tight into a 1-1/2" NPT threaded opening. A threaded adaptor and rubber tank seal (fits into a 2-1/2" hole cut with a hole saw) are provided if you do not have a threaded opening available.

* Assemble Push-to-Lock Elbow onto 1-1/2" PVC Plug Assembly, and bubbler assembly to rigid tubes and sleeves. You may cut to suit tank depth, or leave full-length.

Air Pump Installation:

* Ten feet of air hose is included. Always install the air pump higher than the holding tank, and on a solid, smooth, flat and dry surface. If you choose to install the air pump more than ten feet from the tank, use 3/16" ID x 5/16" OD flexible air tube (available from GROCO). Avoid sharp bends and sags in the air-line.

* Choose a solid mount surface to minimize audible air pump vibration.

* The back of the pump has "hook and loop" tape already in place. Clean the mount surface with alcohol to assure good adhesion. Peel off the backing and press the pump enclosure firmly onto the mount surface.

* Connect the air hose to the air pump nipple, and to the tank-mounted PVC plug assembly. Remember to push the hose FIRMLY into the Push-to-Lock fitting.

Electrical, DC Models:

Sweettank® uses just 3-watts of power at 12VDC. Provide 18-gauge marine grade wire from the electrical distribution panel to the terminal block on the air pump. Use ring connectors

for all electrical connections. A 1-amp fuse is provided.

Electrical, AC Models:

Sweettank® uses just 5-watts of power at 120VAC. MAKE POWER CONNECTION WITH AC POWER OFF. Remove the air pump cover and feed 3-conductor 18-gauge marine grade wire from the elec-trical distribution panel to the terminal block inside the air pump enclosure. Use ring connectors for all electrical connections. A 1-amp fuse is provided.

Operation:

Apply power by turning on the circuit breaker at the power distribution panel. Sweettank® will run and begin the odor neutralization process - within a few hours the holding tank will be odor-free. Allow Sweettank® to operate continuously, even when the tank is empty.

Maintenance:

Two types of bubblers have been used. Annual cleaning of the bubbler assembly is recommended. The multi-colored bubbler is sectional and can be unscrewed for cleaning. If you have a black U-shaped tube bubbler, rinse it thoroughly while squeezing in warm running water.

Winterization:

Freezing conditions will not damage any of the Sweettank® components. Winterization is not required.

Parts Included with Sweettank® Kit

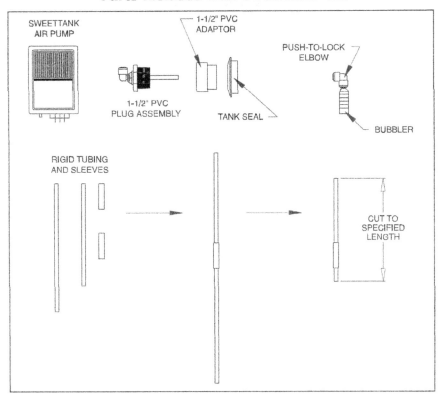

SWEETTANK
AIR PUMP

1-1/2" PVC
ADAPTOR

PUSH-TO-LOCK
ELBOW

1-1/2" PVC
PLUG ASSEMBLY

TANK SEAL

BUBBLER

RIGID TUBING
AND SLEEVES

CUT TO
SPECIFIED
LENGTH

Tank-Top Installation

VENT TO
PORT AND STBD

AERATION PUMP
AND CONTROL

WASTE TO TANK
FROM TOILETS

PUMP BY
OTHERS

WASTE FROM TANK

AERATION TUBE
IS ALWAYS
SUBMERGED

FIGURE-1

Tank-Side Installation

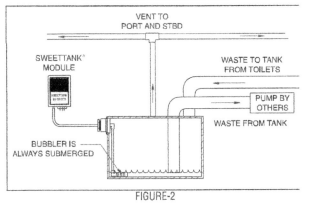

VENT TO
PORT AND STBD

SWEETTANK®
MODULE

WASTE TO TANK
FROM TOILETS

PUMP BY
OTHERS

WASTE FROM TANK

BUBBLER IS
ALWAYS SUBMERGED

FIGURE-2

Appendix B

EQUIPMENT & ACCESSORIES MANUFACTURERS

EQUIPMENT AND ACCESSORIES MANUFACTURERS

Air Head
Eos Design LLC
775 Main St, #481, Westbrook, ME 04098
Phone: 740-392-3642
Email: wboat@airheadtoilet.com
www.airheadtoilet.com

Australian Global Services (Aussieglobe)
The Uniseal Warehouse
3050 Dyer Blvd Ste 170
Kissimmee, FL. 34741
Phone: 321-527-2558
www.aussieglobe.com

Blake Lavac
St. Brendan's Isle, Inc.
411 Walnut Street
Green Cove Springs, FL 32043-3443
Phone: 800-544-2132 or 904-284-1203
Fax: 904-284-4472
www.Lavac.com

The Bosworth Company
930 Waterman Avenue
East Providence, RI 02914
Phone: 888-438-1110 or   401-438-1110
Fax: 401-438-2713
Email: info@thebosworthco.com
www.thebosworthco.com

Dometic Corporation/SeaLand Technology
Dometic Corporation, Sanitation Division
P.O. Box 38
Big Prairie, OH 44611
Phone: 800-321-9886 or 330-439-5550
Fax: 330-496-3097
Email: sealand@dometic.com
www.dometicsanitation.com

Forespar Products Corporation
22322 Gilberto
Rancho Santa Margarita, CA 92688
Phone: 800.266.8820 or 949.858.8820
Fax: 949.858.0505
Email: salestechsupport@forespar.com
www.forespar.com

Gross Mechanical Laboratories (GROCO)
450 Marion Quimby Drive,
Stevensville, MD 21666
Phone: 410-604-3800
Fax: 443-249-4030
www.groco.net

Jabsco
(Xylem/ Jabsco)
Xylem Flow Control
100 Cummings Center, Ste. 535-N
Beverly, MA 01915
Tel: +1 978 281 0573   Fax: +1 978 281-4320
www.xylemflowcontrol.com

Nature's Head
Nature's Head, Inc.
PO Box 250
Van Buren, OH 45889
O(251) 295-3043
419-299-3032
Email: sales@natureshead.net
http://natureshead.net

Odorlos
Valterra Products, LLC
15230 San Fernando Mission Blvd. #107
Mission Hills, CA 91345
Phone: (818) 898-1671
Fax: (818) 361-5389
http://www.valterra.com

Profile Tank Level Monitors
Ferriello Sales LLC
6752 West Gulf to Lake Hwy #232
Crystal River, Florida 34429
Phone: 435-656-0042
Email: dennis@ferriellosales.com
www. ferriellosales.com

PureAyre
Clean Earth, Inc.
21809 95th Pl S,
Kent, WA 98031
Phone: 877-PUREAYRE (787-3297)
E-mail: info@PureAyre.com
http://www.pureayre.com

EQUIPMENT AND ACCESSORIES MANUFACTURERS

Raritan Engineering
530 Orange St.
Millville, NJ 08332
Phone: 856-825-4900

3101 SW Second Ave.
Ft. Lauderdale, FL 33315
Phone: 1-954-525-0378
Email: sales@raritaneng.com
Web: raritaneng.com

Ronco Plastics
5022 Parkway Loop Ste.B
Tustin, CA. 92780
Phone: 714.259.1385
Fax: 714.259.0759
Email: roncoinc@ronco-plastics.net
www.ronco-plastics.net

Thetford Marine
Thetford Corporation
7101 Jackson Road
Ann Arbor MI 48103
Phone: Tech Service 800 444 7210 Option 2
           Warranty 800-444 7210 Option 3
           Consumer Services 800 543 1219
           Outside USA 734 997 6569
Fax: 734 769 2332
www.thetfordmarine.com

Triple-M Plastics
Warrens Way
West Kennebunk, ME 04094
P.O. Box 319
Phone: 800-873-7767
Fax: 207-985-8012
Email: triplemplastics@outlook.com
www.triplemplastics.us

INDEX

Lightning Source UK Ltd.
Milton Keynes UK
UKHW052110021021
391581UK00005B/41

9 781892 399786